Basic Principles and Pract
of Microprocessors

CW00918318

Basic Principles and Practice of Microprocessors

Second Edition
D E Heffer, G A King and D C Keith

Department of Systems and Communication Engineering
Southampton Institute of Higher Education

Edward Arnold
A division of Hodder & Stoughton
LONDON MELBOURNE AUCKLAND

© 1986 D.E. Heffer, G.A. King and D.C. Keith

First published in Great Britain 1981
Reprinted 1981 (twice), 1982, 1985 (twice)
Second edition 1986, 1989

British Library Cataloguing in Publication Data

Heffer, D.E.
  Basic principles and practice of microprocessors.
  — 2nd ed.
  1. Microprocessors
  I. Title   II. King, G.A.   III. Keith, D.C.
  621.3819'5835   TK7895.M5

ISBN 0-7131-3569-7

Typeset in 10/11 Times Compugraphic
by Colset Private Ltd, Singapore
Printed and bound in Great Britain for Edward Arnold,
the educational academic and medical publishing division of
Hodder and Stoughton Limited,
41 Bedford Square, London WC1B 3DQ by
J.W. Arrowsmith Ltd, Bristol

Preface to First Edition

Microelectronics is increasingly pervading all aspects of industry, education and the home. A leading example of microelectronic techniques is the microprocessor, and as its use increases the need for knowledge and understanding will also grow.

This book seeks to satisfy the demand by firstly describing the general basic principles and then expanding to cover the implementation of these principles in real products. The treatment is designed to be suitable for Technicians and Technician Engineers as well as students of electronics and keen hobbyists. Such readers will, if they have access to a microcomputer, gain additionally from tackling the machine code exercises at the end of the book.

The advent of the microelectronics units of the Technician Education Council has been considered during the preparation, and considerable correlation will be found between the unit contents and the text.

The authors wish to thank Mary Grigg and Deborah Shapland for their help in the preparation of the material. Acknowledgement is also due to the Intel, Motorola, Zilog, Rockwell and Western Digital Corporations for their permission to reproduce diagrams of their products.

1980

GAK
DEH
DCK

Preface to Second Edition

One of the fastest moving industries in terms of the development of new products is that involving Electronics and Computing Technology. The purpose of this second edition is to maintain the relevance of the text by expanding the material where greater practical use is now being made of that knowledge. An example of such an area is in permanent data storage. Nowadays many microcomputers are provided with floppy disc backing stores instead of tape systems. Overall, because all computer users now have equipment that is more sophisticated than before, there will be other similar examples. The second edition recognises this change by introducing a new chapter wholly concerned with the hardware and software aspects of disc based operation.

Another update area is that of central processors themselves. The processors covered have been brought up to date as far as 8 bit systems are concerned, and a representative 16 bit processor is now described.

A new approach has been taken in dealing with input/output data transfer methods. The aim was to introduce the reader to input/output devices more gradually, explaining more basic principles before moving to the complexities of commercial products.

Thanks and acknowledgement are once again due to Mary Grigg for artwork and patience. The authors wives must also be thanked for their encouragement and help in preparing the material.

1986   GAK
                                                                        DEH
                                                                        DCK

Contents

1
What is a microprocessor?

The microprocessor is essentially the product of twenty years of research and development in two allied fields: digital computers and semiconductor technology. Consisting of many thousands of transistors incorporated into an integrated circuit, the microprocessor is a single device capable of carrying out many of the basic operations of a digital computer.

The cost of an integrated circuit is generally related inversely to its production volume: circuits similar to the complexity of a microprocessor are expensive because of their restricted market. The microprocessor is a single component having the ability to perform a wide variety of different functions, similar to a standard digital computer, thus opening up a vast range of possible applications. This in turn provides the volume market necessary to make it an attractive low-cost device.

With the price of a microprocessor being quoted in pounds rather than tens or hundreds of pounds, it is possible to make the mistake of assuming that this figure represents the major element of cost in any system employing such a device. This is not true. Considerable man-hours, together with many additional circuits and equipment, are required to make the device 'work'. The finished product therefore costs many times more than the integrated circuit itself. Despite this, the microprocessor-based system is still highly cost-effective, with possible economic applications pervading industry, commerce, and the home. In less than a decade it has influenced every aspect of modern technological society; from toys to cars, sewing machines to factory automation, television video games to office word processors, and even in the design of the digital computer itself.

The use of what is essentially a small-scale digital computer as the heart of most electronic equipment is becoming a reality in a very short period of time.

1.1 Concepts of digital computing

To understand a microprocessor it is first necessary to appreciate the fundamental concepts and operation of a digital computer. A simple definition of a computer is an electronic device that can accept and process data by implementing sequentially a set of stored instructions. Such a device will in the main be made up of standard digital circuits such as logic gates, flip-flops, counters, and registers. Stored instructions and data consist of **binary digits** or **bits**, represented by 1s and 0s and formed into groups or **words**. The number of bits that make up a word varies from computer to computer; 4-, 8-, 16- or 32-bit word lengths are common.

Each instruction has a unique binary code group; the computer will recognise the binary pattern and will carry out a specific operation such as adding two numbers together, storing an arithmetic result in a stipulated device or taking in data from an external unit. Many other operations are possible, some of which will be discussed when specific microprocessor devices are examined.

The binary information contained in a computer is referred to as a **program** and will consist of two main parts: firstly the set of instructions that will cause a desired task to be carried out automatically, and secondly the data upon which the instructions are required to operate. For example, consider the task of adding any two numbers together. A general set of instructions can be produced that, when implemented, will carry out this task. However, the computer must also have the two numbers or data which it is required to process.

A simple example of a program using 4-bit words is illustrated below.

Instruction	Binary code	Computer action
1st instruction	1001	Accepts number from keyboard
2nd instruction	0111	Holds number in special device
3rd instruction	1001	Accepts number from keyboard
4th instruction	0101	Adds two numbers together
5th instruction	0010	Feeds result to a numerical output display

Notice that because the actions caused by the first and third instructions are the same, their respective binary codes are identical. Data in this program consists of the two numbers fed in from the keyboard. Generally data does not always have to be numerical; it can also be textual as long as the words or characters are expressed as binary codes. One of the most important aspects of computer operation is recognising the difference between a binary word that is to be treated as an instruction and a word that is to be handled as data.

The most important characteristic of the digital computer is that it is a general-purpose device capable of being used in a number of different applications. By changing the stored program, the same machine can be used to implement totally different tasks, from calculating salary details one moment to maintaining stock records the next. Although in certain cases justification can be made for a dedicated computer system carrying out a number of fixed tasks under the control of a permanently-stored resident program, the multi-role possibility of a digital computer enhances both its cost-effectiveness and its flexibility.

1.2   From digital computer to microprocessor

Recognition as the first digital computer is normally given to a machine called ENIAC (Electronic Numerical Integrator and Calculator) which was designed and built at the University of Pennsylvania in the early 1940s. It used about 18 000 thermionic valves, was housed in a room approximately 20 × 10 m and weighed over 30 tonnes. Unfortunately, poor reliability developed as the major operational problem of all the early computers. Because of the large number of components involved and the finite life of a thermionic valve, the mean time between failure was typically only minutes.

In 1948 the transistor was invented by William Shockley, and this soon began to influence the computer industry. By the early 1960s a second generation of digital computers was being manufactured using the new 'solid-state' technology. Although the circuits were based on the germanium transistor, which has many disadvantages, reliability was substantially improved and the digital computer began to become a commercially feasible proposition.

In the mid-1960s a major technological breakthrough took place within the semiconductor industry. Using an advanced version of transistor fabrication techniques it became possible to produce on a single silicon wafer an integrated circuit (IC) consisting of a number of interconnected transistors. The new, third generation of computers based on this integrated circuit technology was improved by increased reliability, reduced size and a substantial saving in cost.

The types of computers being designed then began to diversify, and this trend continues to the present day. On the one hand there are the **main-frame** computers, which are machines capable of handling and storing large amounts of information, or of carrying out complex calculations at high speed. On the other hand, the integrated circuit made possible a low-cost computer which is slower in operation and which has limited facilities but which is perfectly adequate for many applications. Such a machine is referred to as a **minicomputer**. Growth in popularity over the years has resulted in this type of computer being developed to the extent that it is now faster and more flexible than many of its mainframe counterparts of the 1960s.

One of the major parts of any digital computer is the **central processing unit** or CPU. All arithmetic calculations and logic decisions take place in the CPU, and it is from this device that most control signals emanate. In a minicomputer the CPU would typically consist of a number of ICs connected together on a printed circuit board. However, in 1969 a calculator manufacturer approached the Intel Corporation to discuss the design of a large-scale integrated (LSI) circuit for use in a calculator. The resulting product consisted of a single integrated circuit or **chip** that performed all the necessary arithmetic and control operations in accordance with a stored program. Such an IC had similar operating features to the CPU of a minicomputer and was consequently called a **micro-processor**. This single integrated circuit has been popularised by the mass media and dubbed the 'silicon chip'.

The first microprocessor was known as type number 4004 and had a 4-bit instruction and data word length. Intel marketed this device in non-calculator applications, and the first generation of microprocessor-based systems was then developed. The 4004 was shortly followed by an 8-bit microprocessor type 8008. This was a more general device and had a set of instruction words very similar to those of a minicomputer. A year later the 8080 was made available: an 8-bit device operating twenty times faster than its 8008 predecessor. In 1974 Motorola introduced the 8-bit 6800 microprocessor which had considerably simplified power supply requirements. Over the next few years the 6800 and 8080 developed as the two market leaders despite the entry of other manufacturers into the field. Companies such as Fairchild, Texas, Signetics, RCA, National Semiconductor, Zilog and Mostek have all produced improved devices since the appearance in 1972 of the 4004. These improvements are generally that more facilities are now available within a single integrated circuit; that operation is faster; that the machines use a 16-bit word length or that they have extended arithmetic capability. Since 1972, the complexity of microprocessors has doubled every two years.

In terms of present usage the 8-bit microprocessor is still dominant with the Motorola 680X, Mostek 65XX, Zilog Z80 and Intel 808X sharing a large slice of the market. The main thrust of the 16-bit microprocessor has still to come, but both Motorola and Intel have powerful 16-bit machines in the 68000 and 80286 which will be increasingly used where a greater data processing power or speed requirement is necessary.

1.3 Microprocessor or microcomputer?

By connecting a microprocessor chip with other integrated circuits and components it is possible to produce a microcomputer. This device, while operating in a similar manner to a minicomputer, is considerably cheaper but slower in operation and less comprehensive. However, these differences are diminishing, and the latest generation of microcomputers are as fast as and have nearly as many capabilities as the minicomputers of only a few years ago.

Provided that suitable facilities are available, it is possible to reprogram a microcomputer in the same way as a minicomputer or main-frame machine. However, other types of computers may be used as dedicated systems with fixed programs, and it is also possible to use a microprocessor in this way. Because of the low cost of a microprocessor chip, the greatest potential growth area is in those applications where a microprocessor, in conjunction with other components, carries out a fixed task under the control of a permanently stored program. Such a system is commonly called a **microprocessor-based** or **embedded microprocessor system**, leaving the word 'microcomputer' to be applied to those systems where reprogramming and multi-task capability are intended and easily obtainable. Unfortunately, in many cases the words microcomputer and microprocessor have become synonymous, resulting in the word microprocessor being used to describe the single CPU integrated circuit (correct usage), *or* the microprocessor-based system *or* the microcomputer.

2
Components of a microprocessor system

Irrespective of whether the equipment is a general-purpose microcomputer or a microprocessor-based system, similar functional building blocks will be used; these are shown in Fig. 2.1. The individual devices that go to make up the blocks are referred to as items of **hardware**. Inevitably, internal organisation and design of the hardware varies considerably between manufacturers and according to specific requirements. This chapter gives a general overview of a microprocessor system, while later chapters will deal with each main area in more detail.

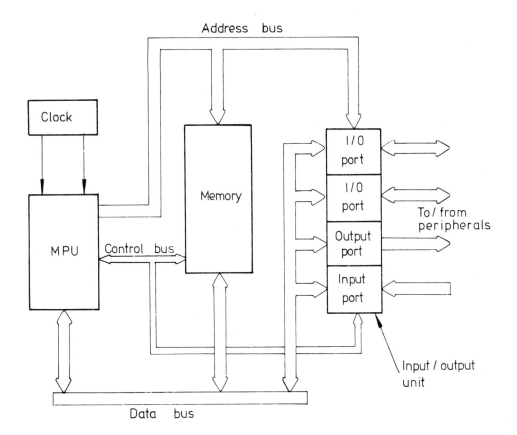

Fig. 2.1   Main functional blocks of a microprocessor system

2.1   Main memory

The internal memory unit is often likened to a collection of pigeon holes, each one holding a binary word representing data or an instruction. The pigeon holes are referred to as **memory** or **store locations,** and to enable reference to be made to a specific memory location, each is identified by its own unique address. A simple example of this concept is shown in Table 2.1, where the store location address is shown in binary form and the contents of a location is an 8-bit word.

Table 2.1   Concept of main memory

Address of memory location	Contents of memory location
0000	00011001
0001	10010001
0010	11110000
0011	01010101
. .	.
1010	10001100
1011	01100001
1100	10011010

The number of bits stored in each location will depend upon the type of memory device used, which in turn is based on the type of microprocessor. For example, all microprocessors using an 8-bit word length would use memory devices capable of storing an 8-bit binary pattern. This storage of information in main memory is carried out using electronic devices, of which there are two main types: random access memory (RAM) and read only memory (ROM). **Random access memory** has the capability of storing new information in a specific memory location by what is known as a **write** operation. Information retained in RAM can be transferred to some other device by a **read** operation.

To enable a read or write operation to take place very quickly, it must be easy to select the required memory location via its unique address. The term 'random access memory' is obtained from this requirement. However, read only memory devices also have random access capability, although they do not have both read and write facilities. Hence the term random access memory is rather misleading as a specific description for one type of device, and in practice, RAM is commonly referred to as **read/write memory.** One disadvantage of RAM is that the store is volatile, i.e. when the power supply is removed the information previously stored is lost.

In a microprocessor-based system the program must be permanently held in memory so that the set of instructions is immediately available for execution when power is supplied to the equipment. To achieve this facility a **read only memory** (ROM) is used. Here the memory device is preprogrammed during the manufacturing stage, leaving the information permanently stored for later retrieval. Various methods are available for permanently storing information in ROM and these will be discussed in more detail in Chapter 12.

Besides the two types of main memory devices available, a distinction is also made between the information that is held within each type. Programs and data that are held in RAM can be changed very easily and are referred to as **software,** whereas a program of instructions and any data constants held permanently in ROM are known as **firmware.**

In both microcomputers and microprocessor-based systems there is generally a requirement for both types of main memory. The percentage allocation for RAM and ROM will depend upon the requirements for the actual system. Reprogramming and multi-task capability are major features of a microcomputer system, and therefore a substantial RAM capability is required. The function of microprocessor-based equipment would normally be to execute a standard set of instructions held in ROM with only the variable data held in RAM. In these circumstances it is likely that ROM storage will greatly exceed the read/write memory.

2.2 Microprocessor unit (MPU)

This is the single microprocessor integrated circuit often referred to as the **central processing unit** (CPU). It forms the 'brains' of the computing system and performs most control operations as well as any arithmetic and logical calculations. On the arithmetic side, all calculations are broken down into the simplest arithmetical processes. Partial results are sent back to the RAM area of the store to be called for again at a later stage of the calculation. The final arithmetic results may be passed directly to the output, but are more usually sent back to the memory. From there they are passed via the input/output device to the appropriate peripheral in accordance with the program.

Control of the flow of information through the system and of the order in which a sequence of instructions is carried out is also a major function of the CPU. To achieve this, the CPU must interpret the coded instructions contained in the program and initiate the appropriate commands in the various microprocessor units. Commands in the form of control signals flow along control lines, opening and closing the electronic switches which allow the data to feed from one unit to another.

2.3 Peripheral devices

Information consisting of either data or a program can be fed into or retrieved from a microprocessor system via any one of a number of peripheral devices. A list of standard input/output equipment is shown in Table 2.2. This table also indicates whether the device is used for input or output and gives typical speeds of operation.

Table 2.2 Standard input/output peripheral equipment

Device	Input/output	Speed of operation (characters/sec)
Teletypewriter	Input/output	10 (output only)
Visual display unit (VDU)	Input/output	1200 (output only)
Keyboard	Input	Depends on operator
Video monitor	Output	2000
Matrix printer	Output	40–300
Daisy wheel printer	Output	10–50
Magnetic tape cassette player/recorder	Input/output	30–250
Magnetic floppy disk	Input/output	30 000
Paper tape punch	Output	30
Paper tape reader	Input	30

There are three standard peripheral devices where information is fed in manually via a keyboard and output to either a display or a printer; these devices are the teletypewriter, visual display unit and separate keyboard/TV monitor. This last combination provides a very cheap form of communication with a microprocessor system and is used in certain low-cost microcomputers. One disadvantage of VDUs and video monitors is that a permanent record or 'hard copy' of the information fed into or out of the micropro-cessor system is not obtainable. This restriction can be overcome by using a digital printer. Two types of digital printer are available for a standard microprocessor system: daisy wheel and matrix printer. A matrix printer uses a print head that forms a character by a series of dots, with a 7×5 dot matrix being a common arrangement. Daisy wheel printers, on the other hand, use a print head consisting of a plastic disc with radial slots cut in it. The appearance is similar to the petals of a flower — hence its name. Each petal has a character embossed on it and will be moved forward by a hammer mechanism when a print action is required. Daisy wheel printers give a better quality print than their matrix counterparts but cannot be used for any graphical representation.

In microcomputer systems it is frequently required to store on a semi-permanent basis information that is temporarily held in RAM. This can be achieved by using either magnetic or paper tape storage methods.

Magnetic storage methods consist of either a standard audio tape cassette or a flat disk coated with a magnetic covering. Two types of magnetic disk are currently available: the floppy disk and hard disk. A fuller description of magnetic disks is given in Chapter 14. Although both tape cassettes and disks can store large amounts of information, the disk systems are faster in both reading and writing operations. However, the separate machine necessary to record and play a disk is at least ten times more expensive than a standard audio cassette player/recorder.

As well as having connections to the specialised peripheral equipment of Table 2.1, microprocessor systems will very often be connected to standard devices such as digital transducers, switches, relays, alarm panels, numeric displays, stepping motors and valve actuators. This type of list is endless because, in general, any device that either produces or functions on an electrical signal can ultimately be connected to a microprocessor or microcomputer.

2.4   Input/output (I/O) unit

This system provides communication with external peripheral devices. It is used for interfacing and controlling when information is to be transferred between peripheral devices and the microprocessor unit or main memory. Most input/output units have a number of separate outlets or **ports**.

The port associated with each unit can be arranged either to take information in from a peripheral (input port), or to transfer information to a peripheral (output port). A port may sometimes be bidirectional, allowing a two-way flow of information, and may also vary in the number of output lines going to any external equipment. In a typical arrange-ment, binary information may be passed along eight lines, all of which are connected to the peripheral. Such an arrangement is called a **parallel** input/output port. Alternatively, data signals for teletypewriter and VDUs are transmitted serially along effectively one line. In this case the appropriate input/output circuit would be referred to as a **serial** port.

2.5   Bus and control lines

Communication between the different units of the microprocessor system is carried out along address and data busses, and also along various control lines.

The address bus   This consists of up to 16 parallel lines along which a binary code can be fed. The code is used as an address to select either a certain storage location in main memory or an input/output port and hence a specific peripheral device.

The data bus These parallel lines are used to carry data and instructions from one unit to another. The number of lines on the bus will be determined by the microprocessor word length. Because of the popularity of 8-bit machines, data busses of 8 lines are most common, although 4 and 16 bits are also used.

The control lines A number of single control lines are used in any microprocessor-based system to control the flow of information between units. No standard format exists for these lines, with their function and number varying considerably between different types of processor.

2.6 Methods of programming

The final form of the instructions and data on which the microprocessor will operate must be binary signals. In this form the program is in a low-level language called **machine code**. An alternative to this arrangement is to write the program in a high-level language such as BASIC or CORAL. These languages bear a moderate resemblance to a living language (usually English) and are thus more readily learned than pure digital codes. The process of translation from high-level language to machine code is carried out by the microprocessor under the control of a very elaborate program called a **compiler** or **interpreter**. This program can either be held on magnetic cassette tape or disk and loaded into RAM when required, or be held in ROM as a permanent section of the memory space.

Although each system may have its own distinct machine code, a program in any high-level language, say BASIC, may be run on any type of microcomputer system provided that the system has an interpreter for that language. This is one important advantage in the use of a high-level language. A serious disadvantage is that the interpreter takes up a substantial part of the store and the machine takes longer to carry out high-level instructions than it would if they were in machine code. When a microprocessor system is going to be dedicated to a particular task that will not require the program to be changed, or where the amount of storage space is limited, the program will normally be written and held in machine code form.

2.7 Clock

All control operations are governed by the master timing source or **clock**. This is usually a quartz crystal oscillator producing accurate timing waveforms up to about 10 MHz, depending on the type of processor. A number of microprocessors now have the oscillator circuit incorporated within the integrated circuit, leaving the quartz crystal as the only external component required. Where precise timing is not required, such as in computer controlled games, a simple resistor — capacitor timing circuit may be used.

2.8 Hardware layout

A microprocessor or microcomputer system made up from the functional blocks considered so far can come in many different forms. At one extreme there is the multi-board or 'boxed' system, where each of the main units consists of at least one printed circuit board with memory taking up perhaps a maximum of eight boards. All the boards are plugged into a common bus configuration which allows address, data and control lines to go to each unit as required.

A simpler version of the multi-board system is the single-board computer (SBC). In this arrangement the MPU, ROM and limited RAM, plus at least one input/output port, are all available on one printed circuit board.

Finally, it is now possible to get a single LSI microprocessor circuit containing the MPU, a program held in ROM, limited RAM, and input/output facilities. In addition the device contains other circuits which are useful for control work, such as a timer, signal converter, and data selection device.

2.9   Microprocessor-based systems

The following two examples are designed to illustrate how a microprocessor can be used to carry out a simple control function and also as a low-cost microcomputer.

2.9.1   Microprocessor-controlled washing machine

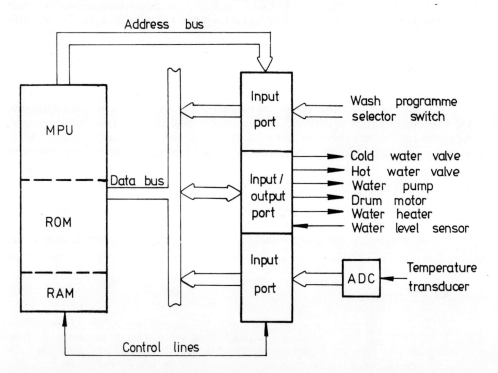

Fig. 2.2   Microprocessor-controlled washing machine

The system is illustrated in Fig. 2.2. At switch-on, the program held in ROM will first take in the binary code produced by the external wash programme selector switch. This data will then determine the wash programme to be executed. Signals will be sent out to the various actuating devices and data collected from the external transducers. Most of the control actions are digital in nature; for example opening and closing valves, or controlling motors. An exception to this is the temperature transducer which produces an analogue signal that varies in proportion to the water temperature change. This type of signal cannot be fed directly into the microprocessor, but must first go through an external conversion device called an analogue-to-digital converter (ADC). In the ADC unit, the analogue signal is converted into a binary number, which is then transferred via the input port to the data bus and finally to the MPU.

   All the instructions for controlling the wash programme will be stored in ROM. Only a small amount of RAM is required to hold the data coming in from the external transducers and programme selector switch.

2.9.2   Low-cost microcomputer

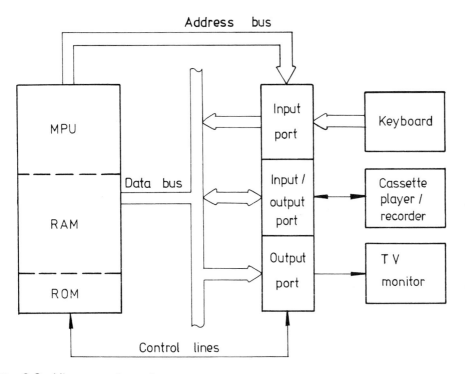

Fig. 2.3 Microcomputer system

The microcomputer system of Fig. 2.3 uses some of the less expensive standard peripheral devices discussed earlier in this chapter. Keyboard and TV monitor are used to feed in and display information, while the tape cassette player/recorder provides a means for cheap mass storage of programs or data. Most of the main memory storage space will contain RAM, so allowing a general programming capability. However, besides the volatile RAM storage there will always be firmware programs permanently held in ROM. These programs allow the keyboard to be used immediately power is supplied to the system, and also control the flow of output information to the TV monitor. Firmware programs carrying out this and other similar functions are often called **operating systems**.

3
Number systems, codes and arithmetic operations

In our everyday affairs we normally use the **decimal** or **denary** system of counting. This employs the digits 0 to 9 as a means of indicating ten fundamental levels or states. For any counting system, the number of digits used defines its **base** or **radix**; therefore the decimal system operates to a base or radix of ten. Despite the widespread use of the decimal system, many other number systems can be used for numerical calculation. Two common counting systems suitable for two-state electronics and digital counting are the **binary** and **octal** systems. The base two binary counting system uses only two digits, referred to as 0 and 1. The octal system uses only the digits 0 to 7 of the decimal system, and therefore has a radix of eight.

To understand the underlying concepts of both the binary and octal systems, it is only necessary to recognise and then apply the general rules of counting which are applicable to all number systems. These counting rules can be formulated using our inherent knowledge of the decimal system.

3.1 Rules for counting

Rule 1   The base or radix of a counting system equals the number of fundamental digits or discrete coefficients available.

Example   In the decimal system with a base of ten the digits 0, 1, 2, 3, 4, 5, 6, 7, 8, and 9 are used.

Rule 2   When counting up in discrete steps, after all the fundamental digits have been used, a column-placing technique is employed. This causes the column with the highest digit in it to return to the lowest state, and the count in the column immediately to the left to increase by one discrete step.

Table 3.1   Column structure for decimal counting system

Column 3	Column 2	Column 1	
		0	
		1	
		2	
		.	
		.	
		9	
	1	0	Reset column 1, increase column 2 by one step
	1	1	Increase column 1 by one step
	1	2	Increase column 1 by one step
	.	.	
	.	.	
	9	9	
1	0	0	Reset columns 1 and 2, increase column 3 by one step
1	0	1	Increase column 1 by one step

Example Table 3.1 shows a column structure for the decimal system, where the absence of a digit in a column infers that a zero is present.

Rule 3 The position of the digits within the columns has a significance in terms of the magnitude of the number being represented. The column on the extreme right, or least significant column, has a weighting equivalent to the base of the counting system raised to the power 0. Each count in the next column equals the base of the system raised to the power 1. Each subsequent column to the left has a weighting increased by one more power of the base.

Example In the decimal system the weighting of each column increases by a power of ten:

Column 4	Column 3	Column 2	Column 1
10^3	10^2	10^1	10^0
thousands	hundreds	tens	units

A number such as 5631 shows that the number is composed of the following elements:

$$(5 \times 1000) + (6 \times 100) + (3 \times 10) + (1 \times 1)$$

or more correctly, using the powers of 10,

$$(5 \times 10^3) + (6 \times 10^2) + (3 \times 10^1) + (1 \times 10^0)$$

Using the three simple counting rules illustrated by the decimal system, a binary number system with a base of two can now be developed.

3.2 Binary. number system

Using only the two fundamental digits 0 and 1 and the general rules of counting, a means of writing an ascending sequence of binary numbers is shown in Table 3.2.

Table 3.2 Binary counting system

Column 4	Column 3	Column 2	Column 1	Decimal equivalent
			0	0
			1	1
		1	0	2
		1	1	3
	1	0	0	4
	1	0	1	5
	1	1	0	6
	1	1	1	7
1	0	0	0	8
1	0	0	1	9
1	0	1	0	10
1	0	1	1	11
1	1	0	0	12
1	1	0	1	13
1	1	1	0	14
1	1	1	1	15

In the binary counting system it is immediately evident that a large number of 0s and 1s are required to represent quite small quantities. For instance, a four-digit binary quantity such as 1001 can be represented in the decimal system by the single digit 9.

Nevertheless, despite this apparent complication, the binary system is universally used in microprocessors. One important reason for this is that electronic devices are most reliable when operating on signals that have only two states.

The sequence of numbers shown in Table 3.2 can of course be continued above binary 1111 by using further columns.

3.2.1   Conversion from binary to decimal

The decimal equivalent of any binary number can be obtained by remembering that each column has a specific weighting. This weighting is based on the radix of the system and the relative position of the column. The weighting of each column in a binary number, represented in decimal form, would be as follows:

Column 5	Column 4	Column 3	Column 2	Column 1
2^4	2^3	2^2	2^1	2^0
sixteens	eights	fours	twos	ones

This means that the binary number 101101 is equivalent in decimal form to

$$(1 \times 32) + (0 \times 16) + (1 \times 8) + (1 \times 4) + (0 \times 2) + (1 \times 1) = 45$$

Using this method, the decimal equivalent of the ascending sequence of binary numbers shown in Table 3.1 can be checked.

3.2.2   Conversion from decimal to binary

Essentially this process consists of taking the original decimal number (integers only) and dividing it repeatedly by two. Each operation produces an intermediate result and a remainder of either 0 or 1. The procedure is repeated until the result is reduced to zero. The binary equivalent of the original number is the remainders in reverse order. As an example, consider the number 373_{10} (the suffix indicates the base of the number).

$$373 \div 2 = 186 \quad \text{remainder 1}$$
$$186 \div 2 = 93 \quad \text{remainder 0}$$
$$93 \div 2 = 46 \quad \text{remainder 1}$$
$$46 \div 2 = 23 \quad \text{remainder 0}$$
$$23 \div 2 = 11 \quad \text{remainder 1}$$
$$11 \div 2 = 5 \quad \text{remainder 1}$$
$$5 \div 2 = 2 \quad \text{remainder 1}$$
$$2 \div 2 = 1 \quad \text{remainder 0}$$
$$1 \div 2 = 0 \quad \text{remainder 1}$$

The binary equivalent of 373 is the remainder read from bottom to top, giving 101110101. By applying the binary to decimal conversion operation this result can be checked.

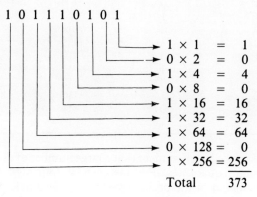

3.3   Octal number system

Using only the fundamental digits 0 to 7, a sequence of ascending numbers can be derived. This is the basis of the octal number system shown in Table 3.3.

Table 3.3   Octal counting system

Column 3	Column 2	Column 1
		0
		1
		2
		.
		6
		7
	1	0
	1	1
	1	2
	.	.
	7	6
	7	7
1	0	0
1	0	1

Conversion of decimal and binary into octal follows the same procedures used for the binary conversion operations. A simple example using decimal 86 illustrates the conversion process.

3.3.1   Decimal to octal

$$86 \div 8 = 10 \quad \text{remainder 6}$$
$$10 \div 8 = 1 \quad \text{remainder 2}$$
$$1 \div 8 = 0 \quad \text{remainder 1}$$

Thus 86_{10} (decimal) $= 126_8$ (octal).

3.3.2   Octal to decimal

$$1 \quad 2 \quad 6$$

$$6 \times 8^0 = 6 \times \ 1 = \ 6$$
$$2 \times 8^1 = 2 \times \ 8 = 16$$
$$1 \times 8^2 = 1 \times 64 = 64$$
$$\overline{86}$$

Thus 126_8 (octal) $= 86_{10}$ (decimal).

3.3.3   Octal to binary
A useful property possessed by an octal number is that it can be converted directly into binary form by taking each digit and representing it by its 3-bit binary equivalent. For the octal number 126 this becomes:

$$1 \quad 2 \quad 6$$
$$001 \quad 010 \quad 110$$

Thus 126_8 (octal) $= 001010110$ (binary).

3.3.4   Binary to octal

Any binary number can be represented in octal by taking the word and splitting it into groups of 3 bits.

$$\begin{array}{ccc} 001 & 010 & 110 \\ 1 & 2 & 6 \end{array}$$

Thus 001010110 (binary) = 126_8 (octal).

Converting a large decimal number into binary can be a long and tedious process. A method of speeding up this procedure is to use the octal system as an intermediate stage. If the original decimal number is converted into octal, then the much easier conversion process from octal to binary can be used to obtain the final binary equivalent number.

Although octal is a perfectly valid number system, it is primarily used as a method of representing long strings of binary 1s and 0s in a more compact form. This system of coding, along with a number of other methods, will be discussed more fully towards the end of the chapter.

3.4   Binary arithmetic

One common function of a microprocessor is to carry out arithmetic operations on binary data. Naturally the complexity of the calculations depends on the task to be implemented. It is not the purpose of this section to provide an exhaustive treatment of binary arithmetic, but simply to show how binary numbers can be represented and manipulated in simple arithmetic operations.

3.4.1   Binary addition

The addition of two binary numbers is the simplest operation after counting. Since there are only two variables, 0 and 1, only four combinations for addition are possible. In the decimal system a 'carry' is generated when the total sum of the numbers to be added is greater than 9, this being the highest decimal digit. Binary addition is exactly the same, except that a carry is generated when the total is greater than 1, which in the binary system is the largest digit. The rules for binary addition are as follows:

$$\begin{aligned} 0 + 0 &= 0 \\ 0 + 1 &= 1 \\ 1 + 0 &= 1 \\ 1 + 1 &= 0 \qquad \text{and carry 1 to next adjacent column} \end{aligned}$$

As an example consider the binary addition of two numbers 10_{10} and 6_{10}.

	Decimal		**Binary**
	10 +		0 1 0 1 0
	6		0 0 1 1 0
Result	16	Result	1 0 0 0 0
		Carry	1 1 1

When adding binary numbers, it must be ensured that the number of bits in the result does not exceed the maximum word length of the microprocessor. If such a condition occurs, an **overflow** is said to have taken place. In the addition example given, if the word length is 4 bits then both the original numbers 10_{10} and 6_{10} can be accommodated; but the final result of 16_{10} requires 5 bits. Under these circumstances the most significant bit may be lost, resulting in an incorrect answer unless special arrangements are made. In most microprocessors the occurrence of an overflow, or a carry generated from the most significant bits, is indicated by a special element in the MPU.

3.4.2 Binary subtraction

The procedure for binary subtraction is similar to that for decimal numbers. When a large digit is to be subtracted from a smaller one, a borrow operation takes place from the column to the left. In the decimal system the digit 'borrowed in' is worth ten, whereas in the binary system it is equivalent to binary 10 (2_{10}). When dealing with the column that the digit has been borrowed from, before the subtraction operation can take place a payback or borrow-in operation must occur to keep the problem unchanged. Although implementing the borrow policy causes some difficulty, the rules for binary subtraction are simple enough:

$$0 - 0 = 0$$
$$1 - 0 = 1$$
$$1 - 1 = 0$$
$$0 - 1 = 1 \quad \text{and borrow 1 from the adjacent more significant column}$$

As an example of binary subtraction consider subtracting 6_{10} from 11_{10}.

Decimal		Binary	
11 −		1 0 1 1	
6		0 1 1 0	
Result	5	Result	0 1 0 1

The binary subtraction did not show the borrow-in and borrow-out operations required to obtain the result. If these are shown, the working is as follows:

Column 4	Column 3	Column 2	Column 1	
1	$^{10}\emptyset$	1	1	− A
$^{1}\emptyset$	1	1	0	B
0	1	0	1	Result

Column 1 and column 2 are straightforward subtraction operations. In column 3, 1 cannot be subtracted directly from 0 and a borrow-in from column 4 to the A digit of column 3 takes place. This, however, is worth binary 10 (or decimal 2) and therefore the subtraction operation for column 3 is:

binary 10 − binary 1 = binary 1

In column 4, the 1 borrowed into column 3 must be paid back in order to keep the number unchanged, and this can be achieved by increasing the B digit by 1. Finally, subtracting the B digit from the A digit in column 4 leaves a result of 0.

Once the basic concepts are firmly understood, binary subtraction is probably more difficult to explain than it is to apply. In most digital computers other methods of subtraction are used which do not entail the difficulties of the borrow operation. One of these methods will be explained later in this chapter.

3.5 Representation of signed integers

For some arithmetic calculations, negative as well as positive numbers need to be represented in binary form. This can be achieved by using either the signed modulus method or the complement notation method.

3.5.1   Signed modulus

In this system, which uses a fixed word length, the most significant bit (MSB) indicates the sign of the binary number. By convention a binary 0 is ascribed to a positive number and binary 1 to a negative number. If the decimal number 45 is to be represented by an 8-bit word, then 7 of the bits will represent 45 in binary form, while the MSB indicates the sign. The following example shows +45 and −45 represented in binary form; for clarity, the sign bit is enclosed in parentheses.

$$+45 = (0)\ 0\ 1\ 0\ 1\ 1\ 0\ 1$$
$$-45 = (1)\ 0\ 1\ 0\ 1\ 1\ 0\ 1$$

In the decimal numbering system, any positive number has an **additive inverse**, i.e. a negative number which is obtained by replacing the + by a − sign. Thus the additive inverse of +45 is −45. The property of an additive inverse number is that when it is added to the original number, the result is zero. Ideally the concept of additive inverse should apply to binary as well as to decimal numbers. Unfortunately in the signed modulus notation the binary equivalent of −45 is not the additive inverse of binary +45.

Decimal	Binary
+45 +	0 0 1 0 1 1 0 1 +
−45	1 0 1 0 1 1 0 1
00	1 1 0 1 1 0 1 0

Using the signed modulus notation the result of adding +45 to −45 in binary form is −90 and not zero.

3.5.2   2's complement notation

One method of achieving a negative-binary number which is the additive inverse of its original is to use a 2's complement notation. To explain this method, assume a 3-bit word length. By using zero as a reference point, and counting upwards in binary form from 000, the decimal equivalent of positive numbers can be considered to have been produced.

Equally well, if we start at 000 and go backwards this can be looked upon as producing negative numbers. The resulting counting sequence produced is as follows:

1 0 0	
0 1 1	+3
0 1 0	+2
0 0 1	+1
0 0 0	0
1 1 1	−1
1 1 0	−2
1 0 1	−3
1 0 0	

Eventually the binary codes produced in the forward and reverse directions will coincide and a conflict occurs. Ignoring for the moment the binary code 100, the interesting point about all the negative binary numbers is that, based on a fixed word length, they are the additive inverses of their positive counterparts. As an example take the decimal number 3:

$$+3 = 011\ \ \text{and}\ \ -3 = 101$$

Decimal	Binary
+3 +	0 1 1 +
−3	1 0 1
0	1: 0 0 0

                     ↑
           This bit is 'lost'

    Disregarding the fourth bit, adding in binary form +3 to −3 gives 000. The negative binary numbers produced by this method are referred to as the **2's complement**. If 100 is allocated to −4, then using a 3-bit word length:

        numbers 000 to 011 are all positive;
        numbers 100 to 111 are all negative.

    This gives a range of −4 to +3. In a similar manner to the numbers produced by the signed modulus notation, the most significant bit is a 0 for a positive number and a 1 for a negative number; but apart from this digit the negative numbers are different.
    In signed modulus, −3 is equivalent to binary 111, whereas in 2's complement −3 is equal to 101.
    If a longer word length is used, then a wider range of positive and negative numbers can be produced. Table 3.4 shows the range possible for a standard 8-bit word length.

Table 3.4   2's complement integers for an 8-bit word length

2's complement representation	Equivalent decimal number	Comments
01111111	+127	Most positive number.
01111110	+126	
⋮		
00000010	+2	
00000001	+1	
00000000	0	
11111111	−1	
11111110	−2	
11111101	−3	
⋮		
10000010	−126	
10000001	+127	Most negative number with additive inverse.
10000000	−128	Treated as negative number but has no additive inverse.

    Although both positive and negative numbers are referred to as being in 2's complement form, the positive numbers are identical to those obtained using the signed modulus technique. It is only the negative numbers that differ.

3.5.3   Rule for forming a 2's complement number
Fortunately it is not necessary to construct a table in order to obtain the 2's complement of a number. The following simple method may be used to obtain the additive inverse of either a positive or negative number.

1)   Take the original number and complement all the bits, i.e. change all the 0s to 1s and 1s to 0s.

2) Add 1 to the result.

For example, to find the 8-bit 2's complement of −85 the procedure is as follows.

i) Find the 2's complement of +85, giving 01010101.
ii) Complement 01010101, giving 10101010.
iii) Add 1 to 10101010, giving 10101011.

Therefore the 2's complement of −85 is 10101011.
Alternatively, to find the decimal equivalent of the 2's complement number 10101011, the procedure would be as follows.

i) Complement 10101011, giving 01010100.
ii) Add 1 to 01010100, giving 01010101.
iii) Find the decimal equivalent of 01010101, giving +85.
iv) As the MSB of the original number was a 1, decimal number is negative.

Therefore the decimal equivalent of 10101011 is −85. This is clearly correct, because the original conversion of −85 into 2's complement form was carried out in the first example above.

3.5.4 1's complement notation
The 1's complement of any number can be formed by simply complementing (inverting) all the bits. The resulting number is not the additive inverse of the original, but by restricting all the positive numbers to the range where the MSB is a 0, all the 1's complement negative numbers will have a 1 as the MSB. As an example, −37 in 1's complement form would be formed as follows.

i) Find +37 as an 8-bit binary word, giving 00100101.
ii) Complement, giving 11011010.

Therefore −37 in 1's complement is 11011010.
Although this method is not used in many arithmetic operations, the term 'forming the 1's complement of a number' is sometimes encountered in microprocessor documentation and programming.

3.6 Binary subtraction using 2's complement notation

In the decimal system, a simple subtraction operation such as 52 − 27 may be expressed as 52 + (−27). By taking the additive inverse of the number to be subtracted, i.e. the **subtrahend**, and adding it to the first number, i.e. the **minuend**, the result is the same as subtracting 27 directly from 52.
An identical type of operation can be carried out in binary form. In this case, the subtrahend is turned into its 2's complement additive inverse, and the subtraction operation is carried out by adding the modified subtrahend to the minuend. These rules may be summarised as follows.

1) Form the 2's complement of the subtrahend.
2) Add the subtrahend to the minuend.
3) Ignore any carry digits generated from the MSBs.
4) Take the result as a 2's complement binary number.

As an example consider the subtraction in binary form for 52 − 27.

+52 in binary is 00110100
+27 in binary is 00011011

The 2's complement of the subtrahend 00011011 is:

$$11100100 + 1 = 11100101$$

Adding the modified subtrahend to the minuend gives:

```
  00110100 +
  11100101
```

1: 00011001

↑

This bit is lost

The result in binary of 52 − 27 is 00011001, which is equivalent to +25.

The most important point about subtraction using 2's complement is that the difficulties experienced in the straightforward subtraction with borrow-in and payback do not occur. The complete subtraction operation takes place by means of complementation and addition.

As a final example, consider the subtraction in binary form using 2's complement for the decimal problem 42 − 54.

```
+42 in binary is 0101010
+54 in binary is 0110110
```

The 2's complement of the subtrahend 0110110 is:

$$1001001 + 1 = 1001010$$

Adding the modified subtrahend to the minuend gives:

```
  0101010 +
  1001010
```

1110100

The result is 1110100. As the MSB is a 1, the result is the 2's complement of a negative number and to find its decimal equivalent the positive additive inverse must be obtained. Complementing 1110100 and adding 1 gives 0001100, which is the binary equivalent of +12. Therefore the result of the binary subtraction is −12.

3.7 Multiple-word integer representation

When a fixed binary length is used to represent a decimal number, the maximum range of integers is limited. An unsigned binary number using 8 bits can only represent integers in the range 0 to 255. If the same number of bits is used to hold a 2's complement number, the range is −128 to +127. By holding as two words a binary number that consists of more than 8 bits, the decimal integer range can be greatly extended. For example, 3867 as an unsigned binary number is 1111001011. This can be split into two 8-bit words with the least significant 8 bits (10010011) held in one word and the most significant 8 bits (00000111) held in the other.

If these multiple words are to be stored in the memory unit of a microprocessor system, they would normally be held in consecutive storage locations.

```
First store location     10010011   low-order data
Second store location    00000111   high-order data
```

When the microprocessor unit deals with binary data, it will naturally require some means of knowing whether the number is represented by a single or multiple word. There is no reason why a very large number should not be held as three, or even more, 8-bit words. In practice, however, this very rarely happens because alternative methods using only two words are available for representing very large and very small numbers.

3.8 Binary fractions

In the denary number system, fractional quantities are represented by using a decimal point to separate the integer part of the number from the fractional part. This same technique could be employed to represent fractional quantities in binary form, but the separator is then referred to as a **binary point**.

Using the position of the digit with respect to the decimal point to indicate the weighting of the column, 35.172 really means:

$$(3 \times 10^1) + (5 \times 10^0) + (1 \times 10^{-1}) + (7 \times 10^{-2}) + (2 \times 10^{-3})$$

If the same technique is used for a binary example, then 101.101 represents in decimal form:

$$(1 \times 2^2) + (0 \times 2^1) + (1 \times 2^0) + (1 \times 2^{-1}) + (0 \times 2^{-2}) + (1 \times 2^{-3})$$
$$= 4 + 0 + 1 + 0.5 + 0 + 0.125$$
$$= 5.625$$

The decimal value for a range of binary bits to the right of the binary point is shown in Table 3.5.

Table 3.5 Binary and decimal fraction equivalents

Binary	Power of two	Decimal
0.1	2^{-1}	0.5
0.01	2^{-2}	0.25
0.001	2^{-3}	0.125
0.0001	2^{-4}	0.0625
0.00001	2^{-5}	0.03125
0.000001	2^{-6}	0.015625
0.0000001	2^{-7}	0.0078125

The general procedure for converting a binary fraction to decimal is simply to add the decimal equivalents of the bits that are set to 1.

For example,

$$1.10101$$

$$2^0 = 1.0$$
$$2^{-1} = 0.5$$
$$2^{-3} = 0.125$$
$$2^{-5} = 0.03125$$

$$1.65625$$

The decimal equivalent of 1.10101 is thus 1.65625.

The reverse procedure of converting decimal numbers to binary can be carried out by a process of successive subtraction. An example for finding the binary equivalent of 0.34375 will illustrate the conversion procedure.

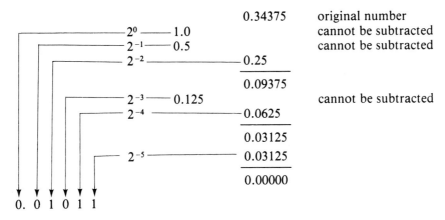

Binary equivalent of 0.34375 is thus 0.01011.

Some difficulties occur, however, when fractions are to be represented by computer words. One problem is that it may not be possible to represent a decimal fraction exactly within a fixed binary word length. Another problem is that a microprocessor has no automatic provision for representing a binary point within a binary number.

3.9   Floating point fraction

This method of representing binary fractions uses two computer words to represent a single valuc. The first word, called the **mantissa**, contains the value of a binary fraction. To cater for both positive and negative numbers this word is represented in 2's complement form. The second word, called the **exponent**, contains in 2's complement form an integer that is used to calculate a scale factor. The following three examples will serve as an illustration of floating point fraction representation using an 8-bit word length.

Example 1

First word	01101000	mantissa
Second word	00001001	exponent

The first word is a 2's complement binary fraction where the MSB indicates the sign of the number.

The second word gives the scale factor which is obtained by raising the base 2 to the power of the exponent.

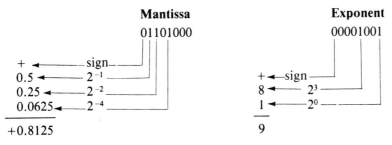

Thus the mantissa is 0.8125 and the exponent is +9. The decimal number is therefore $0.8125 \times 2^9 = 416$.

Example 2

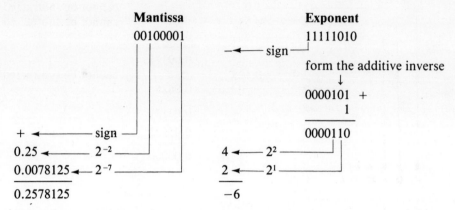

Thus the mantissa is 0.2578125 and the exponent is 2^{-6}. The decimal number is therefore $0.2578125 \times 2^{-6} = 0.00402832$.

Example 3   This example shows how it is possible to convert decimal $+130$ into a binary floating point fraction.

Decimal $+130$ in binary form is 10000010, which is equivalent to 0.10000010×2^8. The mantissa is (S)10000010 where the MSB, shown by (S), indicates the sign. For $+130$ the sign is positive, so the mantissa, expressed as an 8-bit word, is 01000001. The exponent is $+8$, which as an 8-bit 2's complement number is 00001000, therefore $+130$ expressed as a floating point fraction is as follows:

        Mantissa   01000001
        Exponent   00001000

Numbers in a very wide range can be represented in floating point form. The largest number that can be represented using two 8-bit words is

      01111111   01111111
    $+0.9921875 \times 2^{+127}$

This is approximately equal to 1.69×10^{38}.
The most negative number is represented by

      10000001   011111111
    $-0.9921875 \times 2^{+127}$

This is approximately equal to -1.69×10^{38}.

3.10   Alternative binary codes

Within a microprocessor, data is handled and conveyed in binary form without any difficulty. If human intervention is required either for writing the program or for feeding in data, binary representation is not the most suitable medium. To overcome this incompatibility between microprocessor and human, various codes have been devised which simplify the handling of binary numbers and their conversion from decimal into binary form. Providing both man and machine know the type of code that is being used, no problems should occur.

3.10.1   Binary coded decimal (BCD)

So far in this chapter the only type of binary number system considered is the natural or pure binary code, and it has been seen that some of the conversion processes from binary to decimal and from decimal to binary can become cumbersome. By coding each digit of the decimal number into binary form, suitable numbering systems can be devised which are acceptable both to man and to the digital machine. There are several of these types of codes, which are called binary coded decimals. In the most common code, each digit of the decimal number is represented by a 4-bit pure binary code. For example, the decimal number 529 would be represented in BCD form as:

```
 5    2    9
0101 0010 1001
```

The binary coded decimal number for 529 is 010100101001. It must be stressed that this code is *not* the same as the pure binary code for 529. However, the number is in binary form, and the code was a lot easier to produce than the continuous divide-by-2 operation necessary to produce a pure binary number. Similarly, if a decimal number is held in BCD form, the conversion process of binary to decimal is very simple. For example, to find the decimal equivalent of the BCD number 0110000110010111, the number must be split into groups of 4 bits and each group converted into a decimal digit. Thus:

```
0110 0001 1001 0111
  6    1    9    7
```

The decimal equivalent of BCD 0110000110010111 is therefore 6197.

Although this code is very easy to use, its main disadvantage lies in the fact that because it only uses the binary combinations for 0 to 9 it is wasteful in the number of bits used to indicate decimal numbers. An 8-bit word may be used to indicate the decimals 0 to 255 in pure binary. However, if the 8 bits are used to represent a BCD number then only decimal 0 to 99 can be represented.

3.10.2   Octal code

The octal system (see Section 3.3) is used to overcome the difficulty of dealing with long strings of binary 1s and 0s and converting them into decimals. Essentially it is a short-hand method of replacing three binary digits by a single octal digit running from 0 to 7. In the case of a 6-bit binary word the number is split into groups of 3 and converted into an octal digit. Thus

```
011 101
 3   5
```

Binary 011101 is therefore equivalent to 35_8 (octal).

The octal number 624_8 in binary form would be:

```
 6   2   4
110 010 100
```

Thus 624_8 is 110010100 in binary.

The advantage of the octal system over BCD is that no combinations are wasted. Octal coding is commonly used in minicomputers, but in microprocessors an alternative code called hexadecimal is almost universally used.

3.10.3   Hexadecimal coding

This coding system for representing binary numbers is used because of the 8-bit word length found in many microprocessors. By splitting the 8-bit word into two 4-bit groups the decimal characters 0 to 9 can be used to represent ten of the combinations in either group. However, four binary digits can be arranged into 16 different combinations. In the hexadecimal (hex) code, the remaining six combinations are allocated the first six letters of the alphabet; A to F. Table 3.6 gives the relationship between decimal, pure binary and hexadecimal code.

Table 3.6   Binary and hexadecimal notation

Decimal	Pure binary as 4 bits	Hexadecimal
0	0000	0
1	0001	1
2	0010	2
3	0011	3
4	0100	4
5	0101	5
6	0110	6
7	0111	7
8	1000	8
9	1001	9
10	1010	A
11	1011	B
12	1100	C
13	1101	D
14	1110	E
15	1111	F

As an example of representing an 8-bit word in hexadecimal code, binary 10110110 would be coded as follows:

    1011 0110
     B   6

Hexadecimal code for 10110110 is therefore B6.

Finally the binary number for hexadecimal code AF would be

     A   F
    1010 1111

Thus AF (hex) = 10101111 (binary).

4

Hardware devices

A detailed examination of the circuits used in a microprocessor or microcomputer is outside the range of this book. Nevertheless, to appreciate some of the software programming techniques, and to carry out simple peripheral interfacing, a more detailed knowledge of microprocessor hardware is required. To provide such background information, this chapter deals with the characteristics and general action of the common digital circuits used in most microprocessor systems.

4.1 Status flags

A status flag is a device for remembering and indicating whether a certain event has occurred. The standard symbol for a flag, with its input and output marked, is shown in Fig. 4.1.

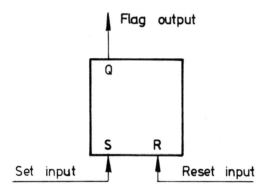

Fig. 4.1 Symbol for a status flag

When a signal is applied to the set (S) input terminal, the flag output will take up a logic 1 level and will then stay in that state even after the signal on the S terminal is removed. If the output goes to logic 1 the flag is said to be **set**. Alternatively, if a signal is applied to the reset (R) input terminal, the flag output will take up a logic 0 level and will then stay in that state even after the signal on the R terminal is removed. In this condition the flag is said to be **reset** or **cleared**.

This type of device can be implemented using standard logic gates and is referred to as an **SR flip-flop**. Figure 4.2 shows a NOR gate flip-flop where the set and reset actions are accomplished by logic 1 signals being applied to the S and R terminals respectively.

One example of the use of a flag is in controlling the transfer of data from the MPU, via an input/output unit, to a peripheral device such as a teletypewriter printer. This arrangement is shown in Fig. 4.3. When the microprocessor executes an instruction to print a character on the teletypewriter, it will first need to ascertain whether the printer is

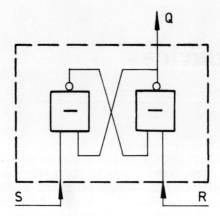

Fig. 4.2   NOR gate SR flip-flop

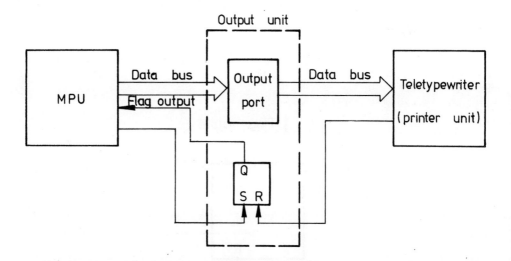

Fig. 4.3   Use of status flag on teletypewriter printer

free to print the character. This is achieved by checking the status flag output. If the flag output is reset the printer is available and the character will be transmitted. Directly data transfer begins, the flag will be set by the output unit of the MPU, indicating that the printer is **busy**. After the character has been printed, the flag will be reset, indicating to the microprocessor that the next character can now be transmitted. So by examining the flag, the MPU can check on the status of the peripheral; flag set indicates printer busy, flag reset indicates printer free.

Flags are not just used for controlling the transfer of data. They may also be used for indicating the occurrence of events taking place within the microprocessor integrated circuit. For example, if the execution of an arithmetic operation results in the answer being negative, a flag will be set. Other flags may be used as illustrated in Fig. 4.4 to indicate the result of arithmetic operations such as a zero; a carry digit generated from a binary addition; or a borrow digit generated from a binary subtraction.

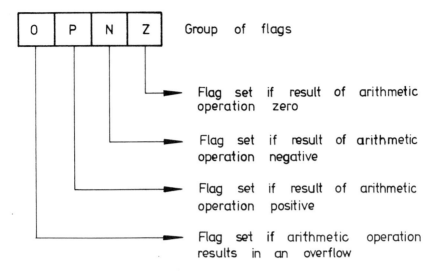

Flag set if result of arithmetic operation zero

Flag set if result of arithmetic operation negative

Flag set if result of arithmetic operation positive

Flag set if arithmetic operation results in an overflow

Fig. 4.4   Group of status flags

4.2   D-type flip-flop

This is a memory element similar to the SR flip-flop whereby binary information in the form of a 0 or 1 can be stored indefinitely, subject to power supply continuity. Flip-flops are also known as **bistable** devices because they have two stable states, i.e. if the circuit is storing a logic 1, it will remain stable in this state until an external signal changes it to store a logic 0. The symbol for a D flip-flop or bistable is shown in Fig. 4.5. The device has one data input (D) and a control or clock pulse input (Clk). Normally two outputs Q and $\bar{Q}$ are available, although both terminals may not always be used. The $\bar{Q}$ terminal is always the logic inverse of Q, i.e. if Q = 1, $\bar{Q}$ = 0 and *vice versa*.

The binary value to be stored in the flip-flop is applied to the D input. When the clock pulse line goes from a logic 0 to a logic 1 (positive-going edge of pulse), the binary value on the D input is stored in the flip-flop and appears at the Q output. After this positive edge, the data can be removed from the D input without altering the stored value. The

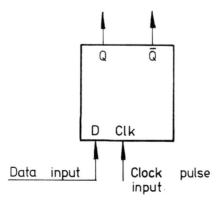

Fig. 4.5   Symbol for D-type flip-flop

negative-going edge of the clock pulse will have no effect on the flip-flop storage action. This operation is summarised in Table 4.1.

Table 4.1   Truth table of D flip-flop

Data input	Q output after clock pulse
0	0
1	1

An alternative type of D flip-flop enters the data on the negative edge of the clock pulse. Although the truth table is identical, there are substantial differences in operating characteristics.

4.3   Registers

A register is a device consisting of a number of flip-flops grouped together and capable of storing a binary word. Various types of registers exist; their differences are mainly in terms of the size of the word stored and the means by which the word is transferred into, and later fed out from, the register.

4.3.1   4-bit parallel register

The symbol for a 4-bit parallel register is shown in Fig. 4.6. The binary word to be stored is placed on the data input lines, D_0–D_3. When the W line is activated (**pulsed** or **strobed**) the binary information is stored in the register. This action is referred to as a **write** operation. In a standard parallel register, immediately a write operation takes place the stored word appears on the data output lines. Registers capable of storing 4, 8 or 16 bits are commonly found in microprocessor systems.

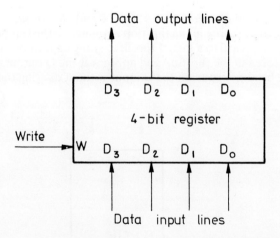

Fig. 4.6   Symbol for 4-bit parallel register

The implementation of a 4-bit parallel register using D flip-flops is shown in Fig. 4.7. In this circuit the write operation takes place when the write line changes from logic 0 to logic 1.

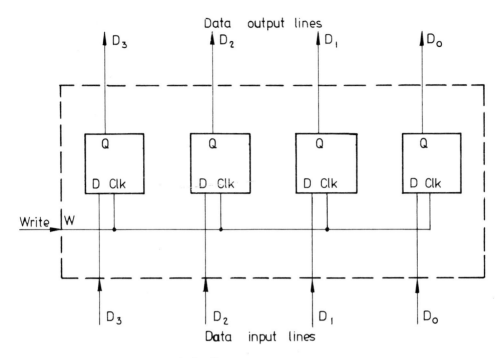

Fig. 4.7 Parallel register using D flip-flops

4.3.2 Parallel register with read/write action

The second main type of parallel register is shown in Fig. 4.8. This has the additional feature of reading the word stored in the register onto the data output lines.

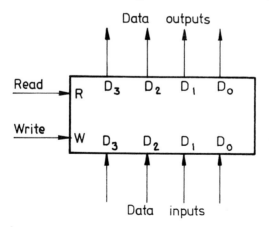

Fig. 4.8 Symbol for read/write register

Implementation of the **read** facility is obtained by taking the Q outputs from the D flip-flops through AND gates, as shown in Fig. 4.9. In this circuit the read line, unlike the strobed write line, must be kept permanently high (logic 1) for the stored word to remain on the data output lines.

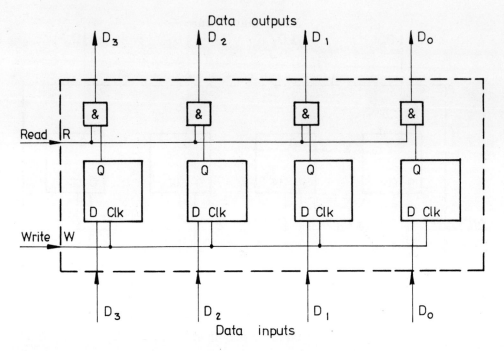

Fig. 4.9   Read/write register using D flip-flops

One important feature of all flip-flop type registers is that a write operation removes all trace of the previous word stored, while a read operation leaves the stored word unaffected.

4.3.3   Shift registers

The major characteristic of a shift register is that the read and write operations can take place by shifting the bits of the word serially from one flip-flop unit to the next within the register. This type of operation enables a serial stream of data, where only one bit is present at a time, to be stored and then fed out in parallel form. A similar operation can be carried out where information stored in parallel form is fed out serially.

Serial input/parallel output   A 4-bit serial input/parallel output (SIPO) register is shown in Fig. 4.10. If the binary word 1001 is transmitted down a line in serial form, then during the period t_0–t_1 a logic 1 is present on the data input line. The application of a

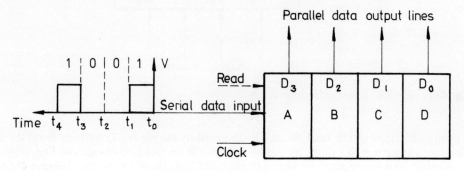

Fig. 4.10   Serial input/parallel output shift register

clock pulse during this period would cause the logic 1 to be entered into flip-flop unit A. During time t_1-t_2, logic 0 is present on the data input line. A clock pulse during this period causes the logic 1 stored in unit A to be shifted into flip-flop unit B, and the logic 0 on the data line to be entered into A. For the time period t_2-t_3 a logic 0 is present on the data input, and a clock pulse applied during this time would cause a serial shift right of all the data. This will result in C holding a logic 1, with B and A holding a logic 0. Over the time period t_3-t_4 the last bit of the word, a logic 1, is shifted into A and all the other data is shifted right one position. The stored word can now be read out from the register in parallel form as a 4-bit word. A summary of the storage action for this type of shift register is shown in Table 4.2.

Table 4.2 Storage action for a serial input shift register: X means the content could be either 0 or 1

Control pulses	Data word to be stored	Flip-flop units A B C D
Initial state	1 0 0 1	X X X X
First clock pulse		1 X X X
Second clock pulse		0 1 X X
Third clock pulse		0 0 1 X
Fourth clock pulse		1 0 0 1

Parallel input/serial output An alternative shift register arrangement is where the data is available in parallel form for the write operation, but fed out serially during the read sequence. Figure 4.11 shows a typical parallel input/serial output (PISO) register.

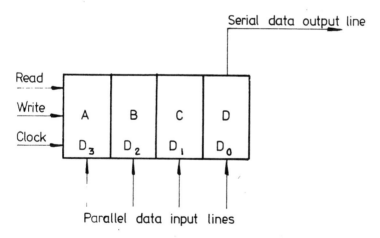

Fig. 4.11 4-bit parallel input/serial output shift register

If the word held on data line D_0-D_3 is 1001, then after a single write operation this is stored in flip-flop units A, B, C and D respectively.

In some registers the D output is directly connected to the output line. If this were the case, logic 1 would now be present on the serial data output. Other types of shift register have buffering between their storage flip-flops and output line. In either case the application of a clock pulse causes all the data to be shifted right one position, and now a logic 0 is present on the output line. The original logic 1 in the D unit is lost and the data now held in the A unit could be either a 0 or a 1. The action for further clock pulses in the read sequence is shown in Table 4.3. Following a third clock pulse, the stored parallel word will have been fed out in serial form.

Table 4.3   Storage action for a serial output shift register: X means the content could be either 0 or 1

Control pulses	Data input lines D_3 D_2 D_1 D_0				Flip-flop unit A B C D				Serial data output line
Initial state	1	0	0	1	X	X	X	X	X
Write pulse					1	0	0	1	1
First clock pulse					X	1	0	0	0
Second clock pulse					X	X	1	0	0
Third clock pulse					X	X	X	1	1

4.4   Device connections to bus lines

A common situation occurs in any digital computer where it is necessary to connect the outputs from a number of different registers or data sources to a set of bus lines. Normally this type of connection would be unacceptable, because if any two devices have different data at their outputs, there will be a conflict as to the correct level on the common line.

In Fig. 4.12, register 1 is being read and its stored data transferred onto the common bus. Register 2 output lines are all at 0, so producing conflicting data on lines D_1 and D_2.

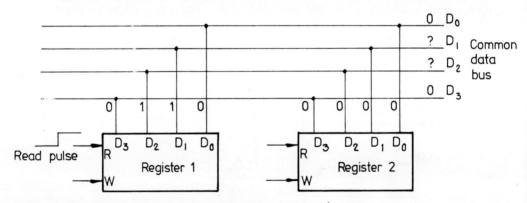

Fig. 4.12   Problem with common connection

The following three methods are commonly used as a solution to this problem.

1)   Wired-OR connection.
2)   Tri-state output.
3)   Multiplexing.

4.4.1   Wired-OR connection
If the output circuit of each register has a wired-OR facility this common-connection problem is overcome. The special property of wired-OR is that if the output of any line is logic 0, this overrides the logic 1 outputs from all the other common lines. In the case of parallel registers with read control lines, all devices not being read will produce logic 1 outputs. For the selected register being read, stored data will appear on the common

output lines, with any logic 0s overriding the logic 1s from the other register outputs. Wired-OR connection can only be achieved by using registers with what is called an open-collecter output, and by the use of a common external pull-up resistor. An example of a wired-OR arrangement is shown in Fig. 4.13.

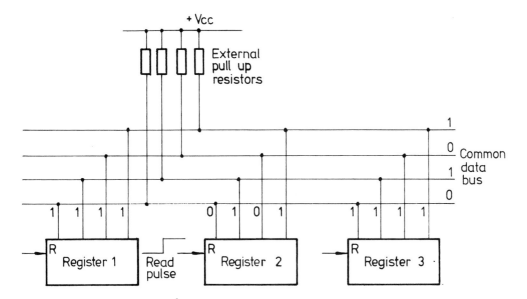

Fig. 4.13   Registers with wired-OR connection

4.4.2   Tri-state output

An alternative method of producing a common output connection is to use a register with a tri-state output. This facility allows the resistance of the output circuit to go to a high impedance state when the register is not being read. Effectively this means that the device is no longer connected to the common bus. When a register is read, its output lines, and hence the common data bus, go either to logic 1 or to logic 0, depending on the word stored. Tri-state output circuits have the advantage over wired-OR that they do not require external pull-up resistors on the common data bus lines.

4.4.3   Multiplexer

This unit is capable of selecting one device, by means of electronic switching, and connecting that device to a common bus line. Multiplexers can be bidirectional, allowing data to pass either from the selected source to the common bus, or from the bus to a selected data receiver. For the simple example given in Fig. 4.14 a binary code set up on the 2-bit control bus could select the signal paths shown in Table 4.4.

Table 4.4   Signal paths for Fig. 4.14

Control line code		Path selected
0	0	Source 0 connected to common bus
0	1	Source 1 connected to common bus
1	0	Receiver 1 connected to common bus
1	1	Receiver 2 connected to common bus

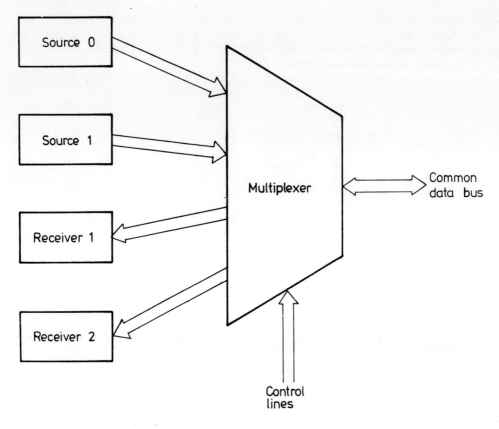

Fig. 4.14 Multiplexer

4.5 Register array

In most microprocessors a number of general-purpose or working registers are stacked together to form an array. These have common input and output connections but individual controls for reading and writing information to and from the data busses. It can be seen from Fig. 4.15 that any 8-bit word set up on the common input bus can be stored in a selected register by strobing the appropriate write (W) line. Likewise, activating say the R_5 line will transfer the contents of register 5 to the common output bus. Each register must have either a tri-state or wired-OR output to overcome the problems of joining together a number of registers to a common line which forms part of the output bus.

4.6 Single-chip RAM

The concept of a register array can be extended to include several thousand addressable registers. This provides the basis for the microprocessor RAM and ROM main memory, where each storage location consists of a register capable of holding one word. In the case of ROM, no input bus exists and only a read facility and output bus are provided. A typical maximum storage capability for a microprocessor main memory would be about 65 000 8-bit words, with the memory hardware consisting of a number of individual

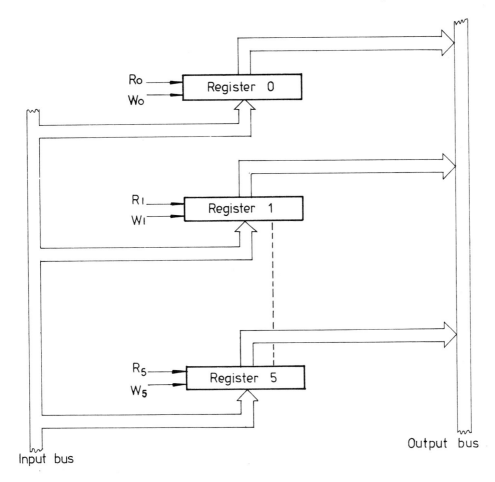

Fig. 4.15   Register array

integrated circuits. An example of a single-chip RAM, capable of storing 128 8-bit words, is shown in Fig. 4.16.

Each of the 128 storage locations has its own unique binary address. Selection of a location is obtained by applying a binary code to the address lines A_0–A_6. This means that address codes 0000000 to 1111111 are possible, which provides 2^7 or 128 different combinations. Control of whether data is to be read from a selected location, or written into it from the data bus, depends on the logic level existing on the single read/write control line. For example, a read operation may be initiated by a logic 1, and a write operation by a logic 0.

To enable a main memory to be made up from a number of integrated circuits, further control lines called CS (chip select) lines are used. The address lines A_0–A_6 from the main address bus may go to a number of identical memory chips. But only if the binary code on the chip select lines is correct will a storage location in that device be selected. When the chip is not selected, the output interface goes into a high impedance condition, effectively isolating the device from the data bus.

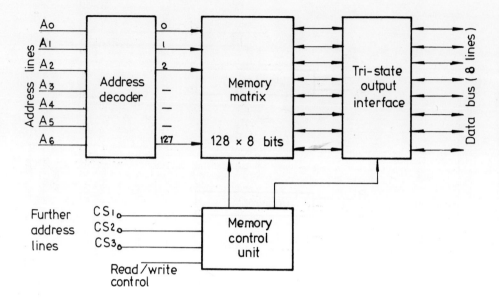

Fig. 4.16   Single chip 128 × 8-bit RAM

4.7   Decoder

The basic function of any logic gate network is to produce an output or outputs only when certain input combinations are present. This type of circuit can be looked on as a **binary decoder**.

In the single-chip RAM of Fig. 4.16 a decoder circuit is required to select the storage location appropriate to the 7-bit binary number applied to the address lines. Similarly the register array of Fig. 4.15 would also require a decoder or addressing circuit; only then could a read or write operation be selective to one register. A logic circuit capable of achieving the type of requirements outlined in the last two examples is shown in Fig. 4.17.

When both A_0 and A_1 address lines are at logic 0, NOR gate 1 output is at logic 1 and all other NOR gate outputs are at 0. Application of a pulse to the common write line will pass only through AND gate 2 to the write line of register 0. The binary word sitting on the common input data line will therefore be stored in register 0. Reading the information held in register 0 can also be achieved with the same binary code on the address lines. This type of logic circuit is called a 1 in 4 decoder as only one out of four possible outputs can be high at any one time. Table 4.5 below summarises the behaviour of the full circuit.

Table 4.5   1 in 4 address decoder

| Address lines | | Gate outputs | | | | Register selected for |
A_1	A_0	NOR_1	NOR_2	NOR_3	NOR_4	read write operation
0	0	1	0	0	0	Register 0
0	1	0	1	0	0	Register 1
1	0	0	0	1	0	Register 2
1	1	0	0	0	1	Register 3

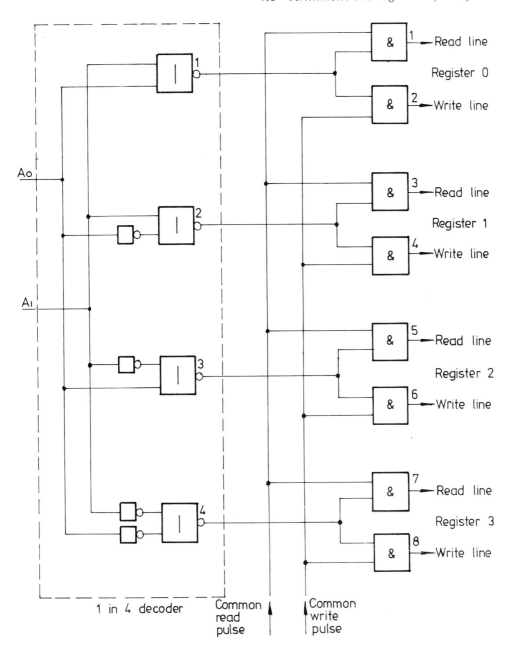

Fig. 4.17 Address decoding circuit

4.8 Arithmetic and logic unit (ALU)

The arithmetic and logic unit usually comprises a binary adder and a system of gates capable of the basic Boolean operations. Such a circuit is a combination logic system having two word wide inputs and one output of the same width. If an 8-bit machine is being considered this means that two 8-bit words are supplied and operated upon by the circuit to give an 8-bit result. It will be realised from the work already done on number systems that the adder portion of the circuit will be able to provide more than simple addition if a few extra features, such as being able to complement one of the word wide inputs, increment an input word and shift the input pattern left or right, are provided. In fact, just these actions allow the unit to add, subtract (by two's complement addition), multiply (shift and add), and divide (shift and subtract). The expected Boolean operations might be OR, AND, EXCLUSIVE OR, and COMPLEMENT.

With all these options, clearly the ALU must be informed which option is currently required. A number of **control lines** from the control unit carry this information which will have been determined from the type of instruction being executed.

An ALU can only perform one operation at a time, using the words available at its inputs. This means that a complex calculation such as $4+5+3+2$ will have to be broken down into a series of simpler sums. Consider an arrangement by which, to do this sum, 4 is first added to 5, yielding a sub-total value 9. The sub-total then has 3 added to give 12 and finally this 'running total' has 2 added to give the final result. A suitable structure is shown in Fig. 4.18.

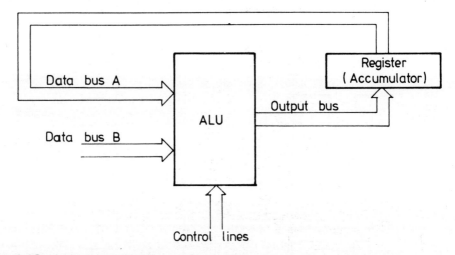

Fig. 4.18   Arithmetic and logic unit

Note that the 'running total' would be kept in a register called the **accumulator**. It is not hard to see why this name is used because the final total accumulates in that register. It is worth noting that, although in Fig. 4.18 the accumulator is shown as a source of data for the 'A' input of the ALU, the 'B' input does not have any connection. Normally, other CPU registers could be selected for this input by means of a multiplexer. The control wires of the multiplexer would originate in the control unit as a result of the current instruction. This allows for the contents of two internal registers to be dealt with.

5
Computer words

A microprocessor deals with words consisting of a fixed number of bits. The most common systems in use at present employ an 8-bit word length, but both 4- and 16-bit designs are also available. A computer word of 8 bits is usually called a **byte**.

The binary pattern making up the word may represent the coded form for:

i)   a number, either positive or negative;
ii) the address of a memory location;
iii) a character or symbol;
iv) an instruction.

5.1   Hexadecimal notation for computer words

Although a microprocessor ultimately functions on binary signals, various problems exist when computer words are expressed in binary form. For example, documentation becomes very tedious, and feeding information into a microprocessor via a keyboard is cumbersome and lengthy if each word has to be expressed as a string of 1s and 0s.

To overcome this problem, computer words consisting of a fixed number of bits are frequently expressed as a hexadecimal code (see p. 26). In the case of a single byte, the 8-bit binary pattern can be shown as two hexadecimal digits. A simple example is as follows:

Binary pattern	1	0	1	0	0	1	1	0

Hexadecimal code	A	6

It is obvious from the example that it is far more convenient to write A6 than it is to write 10100110. Similarly, when feeding information into a microprocessor via a keyboard, pressing the key A followed by the key 6 can be arranged to produce successively the binary patterns 1010 and 0110. These two 4-bit words will be combined and stored in the system as a single byte.

This use of the hexadecimal notation will be frequently found when handling computer words at machine-code level.

5.2   Representation of numerical quantities

If an 8-bit word length is taken as an example, the binary combinations 00000000 through to 11111111 can be used to represent numerical quantities such as signed integers, multiple-word integers and floating point fractions. Chapter 3 gave detailed information on some of these conversion operations.

Examples

a)   8-bit 2's complement integers:

01110110   represents +118
11011101   represents −35

b)   Multiple-word integers:

First memory location   10010111   (low-order data)
Second memory location   00000011   (high-order data)

The complete word is 00000011 10010111 which represents +919.

c)   Floating point fraction:

First memory location   01101000   mantissa
Second memory location   00001001   exponent

This represents the number $+0.8125 \times 2^9$, which is 416.

5.3   Addressing memory

In the most popular microprocessors such as the Motorola 6802 and the Intel 8085, a 16-bit address bus is used. To accommodate the 16 bits within an 8-bit machine, each address consists of two bytes. As an example, consider a memory location represented by the following 16-bit binary address:

A_{15}	A_{14}	A_{13}	A_{12}	A_{11}	A_{10}	A_9	A_8	A_7	A_6	A_5	A_4	A_3	A_2	A_1	A_0
0	0	1	1	1	0	1	0	1	1	1	1	0	1	1	1

The high-order 8 bits of the address (bits A_8–A_{15}) would be one word, 00111010; and the low-order 8 bits of the address (bits A_0–A_7) would be the second word, 11110111.

The 16-bit address word length enables 2^{16} storage locations to be specifically addressed, giving a maximum store size of 65 536 bytes. This is referred to as a **64K store** (1K = 1024 words).

When working in machine code, although it would be possible to refer to the address of each memory location as a string of sixteen 0s and 1s, it is more usual to express the binary number as a hexadecimal code.

Example

Binary address	0011	1010	1111	0111

Hexadecimal code	3	A	F	7

The code 3A represents the high-order 8 bits, and F7 the low-order 8 bits of the address.

5.4   Characters

When a key is pressed on a keyboard a binary code unique to that key is generated. Similarly, if text is to be printed on a teletypewriter, the microprocessor must hold in store a succession of coded binary words. Each unique coded word represents a letter of the alphabet. A common character code used for communication with standard peripheral devices is the American Standard Code for Information Interchange (ASCII). This is a 7-bit code that can represent alphanumeric characters, i.e. letters and numerals, together with certain other symbols and control characters. The full 7-bit ASCII code is shown in Table 5.1.

Table 5.1   ASCII 7-bit character set

Least significant bits	Most significant bits Hex	000 0	001 1	010 2	011 3	100 4	101 5	110 6	111 7
	Hex								
0000	0	NUL	DLE	SP	0	@	P	\	P
0001	1	SOH	DC1	!	1	A	Q	a	q
0010	2	STX	DC2	"	2	B	R	b	r
0011	3	ETX	DC3	#	3	C	S	c	s
0100	4	EOT	DC4	$	4	D	T	d	t
0101	5	ENQ	NAK	%	5	E	U	e	u
0110	6	ACK	SYN	&	6	F	V	f	v
0111	7	BEL	ETB	'	7	G	W	g	w
1000	8	BS	CAN	(	8	H	X	h	x
1001	9	HT	EM	)	9	I	Y	i	y
1010	A	LF	SUB	*	:	J	Z	j	z
1011	B	VT	ESC	+	;	K	[	k	{
1100	C	FF	FS	,	<	L	/	1	/
1101	D	CR	GS	–	=	M	]	m	}
1110	E	SO	RS	o	>	N	↑	n	~
1111	F	SI	US	/	?	O	←	o	DEL

As ASCII codes often have to be stored as 8 bits, several alternatives are possible for the extra bit. The most straightforward convention is to prefix a 0 to each code:

Character	7-bit ASCII	8-bit ASCII
A	1000001	01000001

Alternatively a 1 is prefixed instead, giving a different 8-bit ASCII code:

Character	7-bit ASCII	8-bit ASCII
A	1000001	11000001

Another 8-bit code makes use of the extra bit as a check to see if the representation of the character remains correct during processing or transmission between the peripheral and input/output unit. The value of the extra bit can be chosen so that the number of binary 1s in the character code is always even. In this scheme the extra bit is called a **parity bit**. If the parity bit is chosen to make the number of 1s in each code even, then the code is called even-parity 8-bit ASCII.

There is no reason why a similar odd-parity code should not be used, with the parity bit chosen to give an odd number of 1s. An illustration of even and odd parity is shown in Table 5.2.

Table 5.2   8-bit ASCII code

Character	7-bit ASCII	8-bit ASCII even parity	8-bit ASCII odd parity
A	1000001	01000001	11000001
C	1000011	11000011	01000011
5	0110101	00110101	10110101

Example   The word STOP can be held in memory using 8-bit even-parity ASCII code as shown below:

Memory location in hexadecimal notation	Memory content	
0008	01010011	S
0009	11010100	T
000A	11001111	O
000B	01010000	P

5.5   Instructions

Although each type of microprocessor will have its own distinctive set of instructions, commands in binary code such as add, subtract, input, output and load are to be found in all computer systems. Each bit pattern when removed from the program part of the store and held in the MPU is interpreted as a unique code. This will initiate a sequence of control actions designed to implement the required instruction.

Instruction words will normally consist of one, two or three bytes. The first byte is referred to as the **operation code** (opcode), because this part of the instruction will tell the MPU the type of operation to be performed. The remaining bytes can be either data or an address indicating where data is located. This part is known as the **operand**.

Any microprocessor will have three main types of instructions, each group corresponding to one of the following functions:

a)   data transfer;
b)   arithmetic and logic;
c)   test and branch.

Data transfer instructions are typically concerned with the movement of data between the MPU and storage locations in memory, or with the movement of data between various registers within the MPU.

For any arithmetic or logic operation on data, such as adding two numbers together, subtracting one number from another, or ANDing two binary words, the second group of instructions is employed.

A requirement in most programs is the ability to carry out a test on an item of data. The result of this test will determine the part of the program that is next implemented. Instructions that allow this facility fall within the test and branch group.

A published list of instructions for a specific microprocessor gives the binary and hex codes for the byte(s) together with additional information such as the effect of the instruction. Manufacturers often use symbols and characters rather than a written description to explain some of these effects. A number of symbols in common use are shown in Table 5.3.

Table 5.3   Symbols in common use

Symbol	Meaning
←	'Is transferred to'
( )	The contents of the memory location or register enclosed in the parentheses
←→	'Is exchanged with'
$(\overline{R})$	The contents of register R are complemented (i.e. all the bits are inverted)

When a detailed description of a computer instruction is required, a standard format is often used. An example of this is shown in Fig. 5.1.

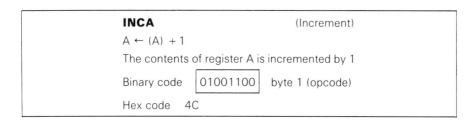

Fig. 5.1 Standard instruction format

Each instruction has a mnemonic, in this case INCA, shown in the top left-hand corner. This is not just an abbreviation of the instruction name, but a group of letters that is used when programming in **assembler** language. Assembler is a level of programming midway between a high-level language and machine code. Also included on the top line is the name of the instruction, enclosed in parentheses.

The next line contains a symbolic description of the instruction operation. In the example, A ← (A) + 1 means add 1 to the contents of register A and transfer the result (back) into register A. There next follows a description of the operation. The final lines contain the binary code and number of bytes that constitutes the full machine-code instruction, and also the hexadecimal code for the opcode.

5.5.1 Single-byte instruction

Operation code (8 bits)	byte 1

From this single byte the MPU must know the type of operation to be executed and the data or device upon which the operation is to be carried out.

Examples of a single-byte instruction

Intel 8085

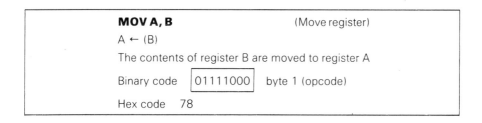

Figure 5.2 shows the result of a MOV A, B instruction held in memory location 0C93 (hex). This action is very often thought of as a **copy** operation, because the contents of one register are copied into the second, leaving the first register unchanged.

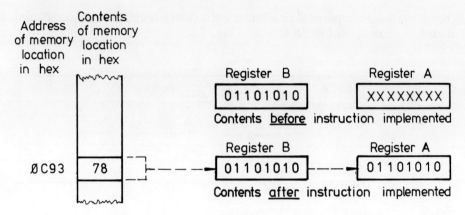

Fig. 5.2   Single-byte MOV A, B instruction

Motorola 6802

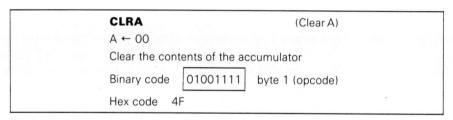

After executing this instruction, the accumulator register will be in a reset condition with all 8 bits at logic 0.

5.5.2   Two-byte instruction

Opcode (8 bits)	byte 1
Data or address (8 bits)	byte 2

The second word of the instruction contains an item of data or the address of a memory location where the data can be found. An instruction which addresses a memory location is said to make a **memory reference**.

Examples of two-byte instructions

Intel 8085

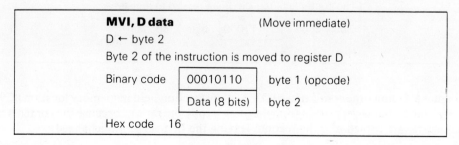

In the MVI, D instruction of Fig. 5.3, byte 2 consists of FØ (hex). After the instruction has been implemented register D will contain FØ (hex) in binary form.

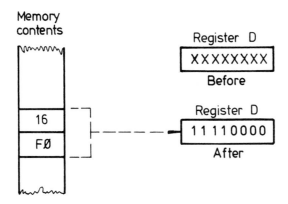

Fig. 5.3 Two-byte MVI, D instruction

Motorola 6802

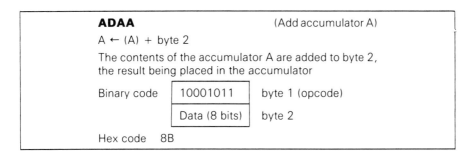

Implementation of the ADAA instruction is shown in Fig. 5.4. If the accumulator A initially holds the binary number 01010101 and byte 2 of the instruction is 00010100, then after carrying out the instruction, the accumulator A will hold 01010101 + 00010100 = 01101001.

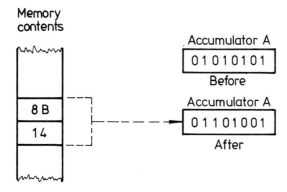

Fig. 5.4 Two-byte ADAA instruction

5.5.3   Three-byte instructions

Opcode	byte 1
Data or address (8 bits)	byte 2
Data or address (8 bits)	byte 3

The second and third words of the instruction contain a data item or the 16-bit address of a memory location or register where the data can be found. Whether byte 2 or byte 3 holds the most significant 8 bits of the data or address word will depend on the microprocessor type. In the Intel 8085, byte 3 holds the most significant 8 bits and byte 2 the least significant 8 bits. In the Motorola 6802 the roles of byte 2 and byte 3 are reversed.

Example of three-byte instructions

Intel 8085

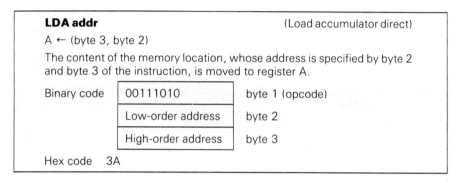

LDA addr   (Load accumulator direct)

A ← (byte 3, byte 2)

The content of the memory location, whose address is specified by byte 2 and byte 3 of the instruction, is moved to register A.

Binary code	00111010	byte 1 (opcode)
	Low-order address	byte 2
	High-order address	byte 3

Hex code   3A

Figure 5.5 shows the position in store for the three-byte LDA instruction and the

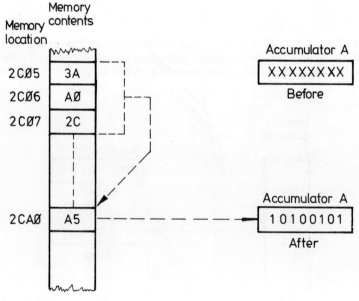

Fig. 5.5   Three-byte LDA instruction

contents of memory location 2CA0 (hex). After the instruction has been carried out, the contents of 2CA0 will be held in the accumulator.

Motorola 6802

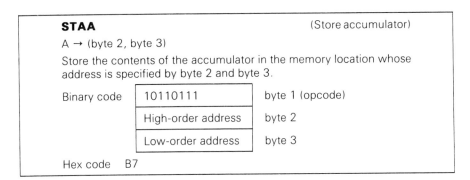

An example of the 6802 three-byte STAA instruction is shown in Fig. 5.6 below. The result of implementing the instruction held in 003E, 003F and 0040 is to place 00111001 (39 hex) in memory location 005E.

An important and useful practical point to remember when using this type of instruction is that the contents of the accumulator are not destroyed. That is, 00111001 still remains in the accumulator after it has also been stored in memory location 005E.

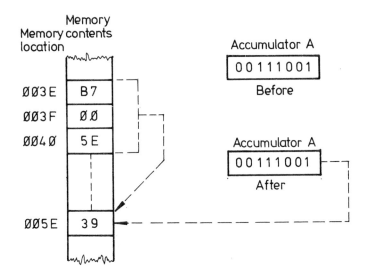

Fig. 5.6 Three-byte STAA instruction

6
CPU structure and operation

The central processing unit (CPU) of a microprocessor system is made up from either the microprocessor alone or the microprocessor in conjunction with a small number of other integrated circuits. The block diagram of Fig. 6.1 is representative of the major components present in a typical CPU. It also shows the system organisation necessary to allow implementation of a series of instructions held in memory. The diagram is not intended to represent the architecture of any specific, commercially-available microprocessor CPU.

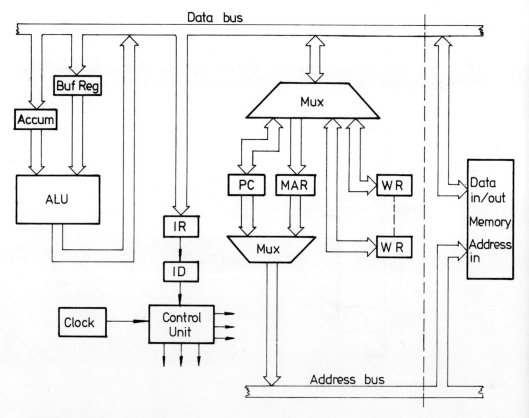

Fig. 6.1 Typical CPU structure

6.1 Function of CPU components

A brief description of the function of all the major devices in the CPU of Fig. 6.1 is given below.

Accumulator (Accum)	This is a specially defined register that holds the result of any arithmetic or logic operation carried out by the ALU.
Arithmetic and Logic Unit (ALU)	A circuit that performs arithmetic or logic operations on either one or two words of data held in the accumulator/buffer register.
Buffer Register (Buf. Reg)	Before a word of data is fed into the ALU, it is temporarily held in the buffer register.
Clock	The clock produces waveforms which may be divided down in frequency and used by the control unit as timing pulses.
Control Unit (CU)	A large number of different functions are carried out by this unit. Examples are: (*a*) setting up the control lines for multiplexers and ALU; (*b*) providing the read/write pulses for registers, memory and input/output devices via the control bus; and (*c*) incrementing/decrementing the program counter.
Instruction Decoder (ID)	The binary word held in the instruction register is identified by the instruction decoder, thus enabling the control unit to send out correct timing and control pulses.
Instruction Register (IR)	This register holds in binary form the opcode byte of the current instruction which the CPU as a whole is executing.
Memory Address Register (MAR)	If a memory read or write operation is going to take place, the address of the memory location being accessed is held in the MAR.
Multiplexer (Mux)	This is the electronic switching circuit that selects the path for information transfer between registers, address bus and data bus.
Program Counter (PC)	This register/counter holds the address of the location in memory where the *next* instruction in the program sequence is to be found. The contents of the program counter can be incremented or decremented by special control pulses.
Working Registers (WR)	These registers can perform a wide variety of functions. Some are used for temporary storage of information, while others are used for specific programming operations.

6.2 Fetch-execute cycle

The complete operation of each instruction by the CPU forms a **microprogram**. This program is split into two main parts which are known as the **fetch** and **execute** cycles.

6.2.1 Fetch cycle
As the machine instruction to be implemented is stored in the memory, the first part of the microprogram is to 'fetch' the instruction bytes from store and hold them in the appropriate CPU registers. The opcode part of the instruction is always held in the

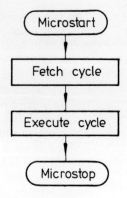

Fig. 6.2   Flow diagram for general microprogram

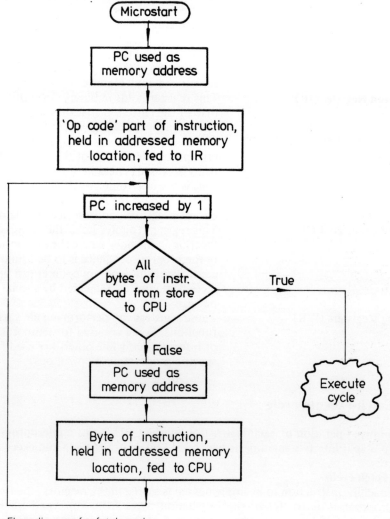

Fig. 6.3   Flow diagram for fetch cycle

instruction register. This enables the control unit to send to other circuits control signals appropriate to the type of instruction being handled. In the case of a two- or three-byte instruction, bytes 2 and 3 of the instruction, as well as the opcode held in byte 1, must be brought out of memory. The complete operation is referred to as a fetch cycle.

6.2.2 Execute cycle
The second part of the microprogram is to 'execute' the instruction held in the CPU. The control actions that go to make up the execute cycle will be determined by the type of instruction and the contents of various registers.

6.3 Operation of the CPU on a fetch-execute cycle

The general CPU structure of Fig. 6.1 will be used to examine step-by-step how an instruction is implemented. The instruction to be considered causes the accumulator to be loaded with the contents of a specified memory location:

Accum ← (M)

This will be a three-byte instruction where the first byte is the opcode 'load accumulator', and bytes 2 and 3 the address in memory where the information to be loaded is held.

An instruction from a commercially available microprocessor that carries out this type of operation is shown below.

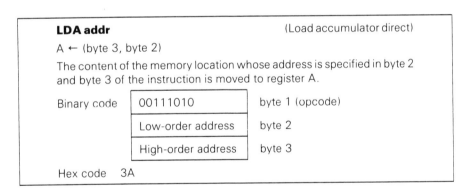

LDA addr	(Load accumulator direct)

A ← (byte 3, byte 2)
The content of the memory location whose address is specified in byte 2 and byte 3 of the instruction is moved to register A.

Binary code	00111010	byte 1 (opcode)
	Low-order address	byte 2
	High-order address	byte 3

Hex code   3A

Other details required for the example are as follows.

a) The three-byte instruction 'load accumulator' will be in store locations 0000, 0001 and 0002 (hex).
b) The data to be loaded into the accumulator is 38 (hex), i.e. 00111000 (binary).
c) The data to be loaded into the accumulator is held in memory location 00AA (hex).

Memory chart
Taking into account all the points mentioned previously the contents of *relevant* memory locations are as follows.

Address of memory location in hex code	Contents of memory location in hex code	Mnemonic code	Comments
0000	3A	LDA	Load accumulator
0001	AA ⎞	address	with the contents of memory location
0002	00 ⎠		00AA.
⋮			
00AA	38	data	Data to be loaded into accumulator.

Steps in the fetch cycle

The three-byte instruction to be implemented is held in memory location 0000 to 0002 inclusive. It is required to move this instruction from the memory into the CPU. Once the opcode is in the instruction register, the control unit will know that the instruction consists of three bytes and that bytes 2 and 3 contain an address which is to be loaded into the memory address register. The individual steps required to carry out the fetch sequence are listed below.

Step number	Operation required	Results
1	Reset program counter.	0000 → PC
2	Transfer contents of program counter to address bus.	0000 → address bus
3	Read contents of store, at address 0000, onto data bus.	3A → data bus
4	Strobe input of instruction register, transferring contents of data bus to instruction register.	3A → IR
5	Strobe output of instruction register, transferring contents of register to instruction decoder.	3A → ID
6	Control unit recognises type of instruction and issues appropriate control and timing signals.	
7	Program counter increased by 1.	0001 → PC
8	Contents of program counter transferred to address bus.	0001 → address bus
9	Contents of memory location 0001 transferred to data bus.	AA → data bus
10	Contents of data bus transferred to least significant 8 bits of memory address register.	AA → MAR
11	Program counter increased by 1.	0002 → PC
12	Contents of program counter transferred to address bus.	0002 → address bus
13	Contents of memory location 0002 transferred to data bus.	00 → data bus
14	Contents of data bus transferred to most significant 8 bits of memory address register.	00 → MAR
15	Program counter increased by 1.	0003 → PC

By the end of the fetch cycle the state of the CPU registers is as follows:

1) instruction register holds in binary form the opcode 3A (hex);
2) memory address register holds the 16-bit address of the data to be loaded into the accumulator, i.e. 00AA (hex);
3) program counter is pointing to the next instruction to be implemented, i.e. 0003 (hex).

The fetch cycle is now complete, and the CPU will automatically move to the next stage, i.e. the execute cycle.

Steps in the execute cycle
Having 'fetched' the instruction from memory and decided upon the control actions required, the instruction is now executed. The steps that constitute the execute cycle are listed below.

Step number	Operation	Results
1	Contents of memory address register transferred to address bus.	00AA → address bus
2	Contents of memory location 00AA read out onto data bus.	38 → data bus
3	Contents of data bus strobed into accumulator.	38 → accumulator

The instruction 'load accumulator' with the contents of memory location 00AA has now been implemented.

The program counter is now pointing to a place in memory where the next instruction is held. After the final execute step in the instruction being implemented, the CPU will move to a new fetch sequence for the instruction held at 0003. The only exception to this would be if the CPU is instructed to 'branch' or 'jump' to another part of the program.

6.4 A simple program

Any machine-code program, no matter how complicated, consists only of a series of instructions that are implemented in a sequential manner by consecutive fetch-execute cycles.

In the previous fetch-execute example, assume that the 8-bit contents of memory location 00AA are arranged to hold the binary coded decimal (BCD) number for two decimal digits.

b_7	b_6	b_5	b_4	b_3	b_2	b_1	b_0
BCD number for second digit				BCD number for first digit			

Each 4-bit group (b_0–b_3 and b_4–b_7) can hold any binary code between 0000 and 1001, allowing the decimal digits 0 to 9 to be represented.

Suppose that it was possible to write a further instruction into memory location 0003 onwards that would cause the contents of the accumulator to be transferred to an output port. This byte could then be decoded as two separate 4-bit words and used to drive a standard numeric output display.

An instruction that provides this type of output facility might be called OUT port, the format of which is shown below.

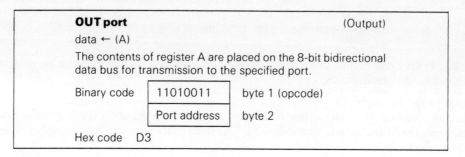

OUT port (Output)

data ← (A)

The contents of register A are placed on the 8-bit bidirectional data bus for transmission to the specified port.

Binary code	11010011	byte 1 (opcode)
	Port address	byte 2

Hex code   D3

Each input and output port connected up to the microprocessor has an 8-bit address that allows any one of 256 different ports to be selected. In the example to be considered, the address of the port to which the logic gate decoder circuit and output display is connected will be port ØØ (hex). The hardware components of the system are shown in Fig. 6.4.

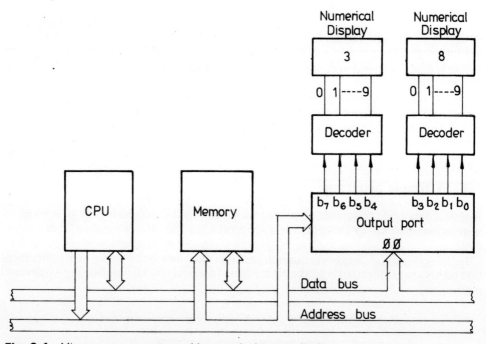

Fig. 6.4   Microprocessor system with numerical output display

On the software side, the machine-code program required, including the new output instruction, is listed as follows.

Memory location	Contents in hex code	Mnemonic code	Comments
0000	3A	LDA	Load accumulator
0001	AA	address	with contents of
0002	00		00AA.
0003	D3	OUT	Output contents of
0004	00	port	accumulator into port 00.
⋮			
00AA	38	data	Data to be loaded into accumulator, and then to output display.

Completion of the fetch-execute cycle for the first instruction results in the accumulator holding the binary word 00111000 (38 hex). The CPU now continues with a fetch-execute cycle for the two-byte instruction held in memory location 0003 and 0004. Correct execution of this instruction results in 38 (hex) being transferred from the accumulator to the output port 00. This port, which is part of an output unit, contains a storage register. The byte 38 (hex) is stored in the register, with the output lines feeding the least significant 4 bits (1000) to one decoder circuit and the most significant 4 bits (0011) to the other. Based upon the binary code being fed to each decoder, one of the ten output lines becomes active; this in turn causes the appropriate decimal number on the output display to light up.

After executing the OUT instruction the CPU continues with the program from memory location 0005 onwards. If the instruction in 0003 and 0004 represented the end of the program, it would be necessary, by placing a special instruction in 0005, to stop the CPU from continuing with any further fetch-execute cycles. The reason for this action is that although no 'official' instructions are contained in memory location 0005 onwards, there will be random 1s and 0s (known as garbage) which the CPU will fetch and try to execute. This may affect the original program, or destroy data previously calculated and held in certain memory locations.

7
Addressing modes

7.1 Introduction

In executing a program the processor fetches the contents of consecutive memory locations. These locations can contain opcodes or data. Each opcode is an instruction to the processor specifying the operations to be performed on the data. The choice of addressing mode determines how the data is acquired from the memory. The basic principles of computing permit references to data to be made in the following five ways:

(a) the immediate mode;   (d) the indexed mode;
(b) the direct mode;   (e) the inherent mode.
(c) the indirect mode;

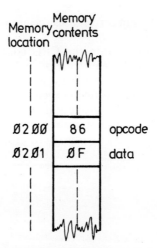

Fig. 7.1 Immediate mode

In the **immediate** mode the memory location immediately following that in which the opcode resides contains the data to be used (see Fig. 7.1). Alternatively, the one or two locations following the opcode may hold the address of a memory location within which the data is to be found. This is an example of the **direct** mode of address (see Figs. 7.2 (a) and (b)). In the **indirect** mode, the addresses referred to in the locations following the opcode themselves contain an address. This address is of the memory location containing the data (see Fig. 7.3).

Many central processing units have an index register or a general-purpose working register that can be used as an index register. The index register may be loaded with an address, and the location in which the data may be found in the **indexed** mode is

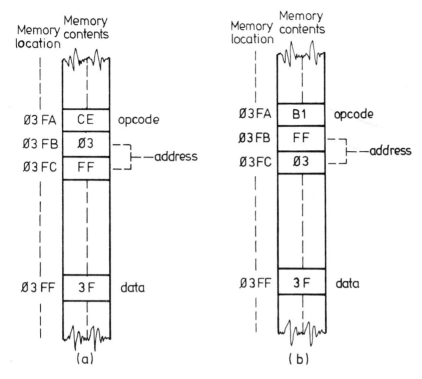

Fig. 7.2   Direct mode

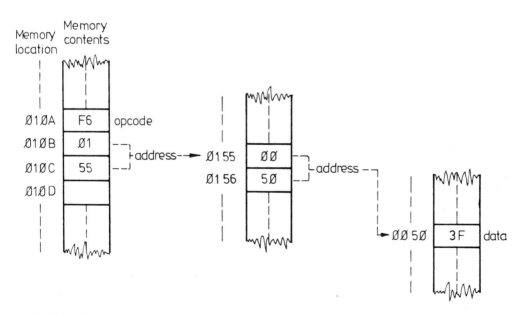

Fig. 7.3   Indirect mode

calculated by adding the contents of the locations following the opcode to the contents of the index register (see Fig. 7.4).

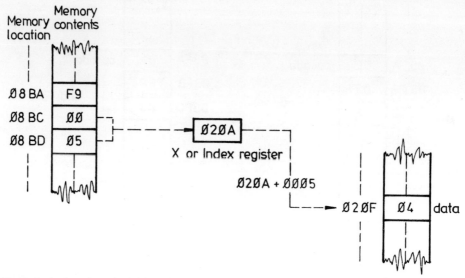

Fig. 7.4   Indexed mode

In any instruction set there will be non-memory reference instructions. In these cases the opcode alone is interpreted as commanding an operation on data already within the CPU. Opcodes such as these are referred to as **inherent** mode instructions.

It should always be remembered that the opcode of an instruction is a unique binary pattern that informs the microprocessor of two fundamentals facts. These are:

1)   the type of operation it is to carry out;
2)   the source location or destination location of the data i.e. the mode of addressing to be used.

In currently available microprocessors there are many variations on these basic principles. The two most popular CPUs of the mid 1970s were the Intel 8080 and the Motorola 6800. Both acted as watersheds in the development of enhanced performance processors. In the comparative work which follows, only the most widely used 8-bit microprocessors are examined, with the differences between each being high-lighted. The microprocessors to be discussed are as follows.

Motorola 6802   this is a hardware enhanced version of the 6800, having an almost identical software instruction set. The 6802 can also be used to appreciate some of the basic features of the later and more powerful Motorola 6809.

Intel 8085   an enhanced version of the 8080 with a compatible instruction set but very different hardware architecture.

Zilog Z80   developed by the same team who were responsible for the 8080 it has many enhanced features over the earlier processor. An extremely popular microprocessor in both home computing and industrial applications.

MOS Tech 6502   designed as an enhanced version of the 6800 it has some software similarities to the Intel 8080. A popular microprocessor in home computers.

7.2   The Motorola 6802 addressing modes

The Motorola 6802 like its parent the 6800 has two accumulators known as A and B. Both accumulators may be used with the full range of instructions, although a given instruction will clearly have a different opcode for each accumulator. There are no general-purpose working registers within the CPU, although there is a dedicated 16-bit index register. The programmable registers are shown in Fig. 7.5.

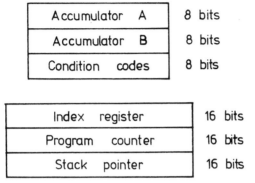

Fig. 7.5   6802 registers

7.2.1   Immediate mode
This takes the form of a two-byte instruction in which byte 2 is the data to be operated upon and byte 1 is the opcode, as shown below.

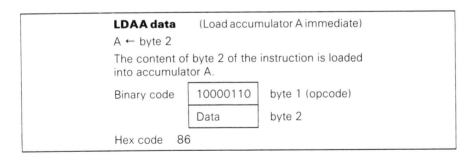

A hex code example

Byte 1	86	Loads the accumulator A with
Byte 2	Ø4	the binary equivalent of Ø4(00000100).

7.2.2   Direct mode
This is a more restricted version of traditional direct addressing in that only references to locations within the first 256 memory locations can be made. This is because only a single byte (byte 2) indicates the address; this is equivalent to $2^8 = 256$ locations. The most significant half of the address always defaults to ØØ (hex) in this mode.

LDAA addr   (Load accumulator A direct)

A ← (byte 2)

The contents of the memory location specified by byte 2
of the instruction are loaded into accumulator A.

Binary code

10010110	byte 1 (opcode)
Low order address	byte 2

Hex code   96

A hex code example

Byte 1	96	Loads the accumulator A with
Byte 2	F2	the data in location 00F2.

In the previous example, byte 2 of the instruction formed a source address of where data
was held that required to be loaded into the accumulator. An opposite operation is where
byte 2 provides the destination address of where data held in the accumulator is to be
stored.

STAA addr   (Store accumulator direct)

A → (byte 2)

The content of accumulator A is stored in the memory
location whose address is specified in byte 2 of the
instruction.

Binary code

10010111	byte 1 (opcode)
Low-order address	byte 2

Hex code   97

A hex code example

Byte 1	97	Stores the contents of accumulator A
Byte 2	C5	in memory location 00C5.

7.2.3   A sample program using direct and immediate modes
The object of the following program is to load each accumulator with a binary pattern,
and store the contents of accumulators A and B in memory locations 0050 and 003A
respectively.

Memory location	Hex code	Mnemonic	Comments
0000	86	LDAA	Load (immediate) accumulator A
0001	04	data	with 04 (hex).
0002	C6	LDAB	Load (immediate) accumulator B
0003	03	data	with 03 (hex).
0004	97	STAA	Store (direct) contents of accumulator A
0005	50	addr	in memory location 0050.
0006	D7	STAB	Store (direct) contents of accumulator B
0007	3A	addr	in memory location 003A.

Although the program is written into locations 0000 to 0007, it could reside anywhere within the addressable memory space.

As a result of running this program, memory location 0050 will contain 04 (hex) and memory location 003A will contain 03 (hex).

7.2.4   Inherent mode
The opcode is sufficient to instruct the CPU to perform some function on data that is already within the CPU registers.

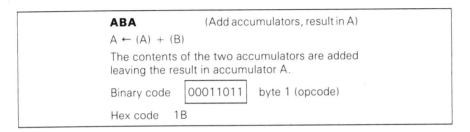

ABA   (Add accumulators, result in A)

A ← (A) + (B)

The contents of the two accumulators are added leaving the result in accumulator A.

Binary code   00011011   byte 1 (opcode)

Hex code   1B

A hex code example

Byte 1   1B   Adds contents of accumulators leaving the result in accumulator A.

7.2.5   Extended mode
This is equivalent to the traditional direct mode addressing where bytes 2 and 3 of the instruction form the address of a memory location.

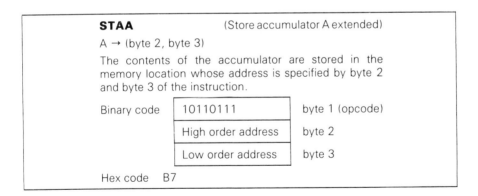

STAA   (Store accumulator A extended)

A → (byte 2, byte 3)

The contents of the accumulator are stored in the memory location whose address is specified by byte 2 and byte 3 of the instruction.

Binary code   10110111   byte 1 (opcode)

High order address   byte 2

Low order address   byte 3

Hex code   B7

A hex code example

Byte 1   B7   Store the contents of the accumulator
Byte 2   A0   in address A00F.
Byte 3   0F

7.2.6   A sample program using immediate, direct inherent and extended modes
The object of the following program is to implement the mathematical equation: $Z = Y + K$, where: Y is the value of variable data stored in memory location 003A (hex); K is a constant value equivalent to decimal 13 (expressed in binary that is 00001101, or 0D (hex); and Z is the result which will be stored in memory location 020C (hex).

Memory location	Hex code	Mnemonic	Comments
0000	86	LDAA	Load (immediate) accumulator A
0001	0D	data	with 0D (hex) — i.e. constant *K*.
0002	D6	LDAB	Load (direct) accumulator B
0003	3A	addr	with the contents of memory location 003A.
0004	1B	ABA	Add accumulators A and B, result in A.
0005	B7	STAA	Store (extended) contents of accumulator A
0006	02 ⎫	addr	in memory location 020C.
0007	0C ⎭		
⋮			
003A	XX		Variable data (*Y*)
⋮			
020C	XX		Result (*Z*)

After the program has been run, the result (*Z*) stored in memory location 020C will depend on the value of data (*Y*) that had previously been stored in 003A. As an example, if 003A contained 15 (hex) then result (*Z*) stored in 020C would be:

$$00001101 + 00010101 = 00100010$$

i.e.   22 (hex).

7.2.7   Indexed mode
The second byte of the instruction is added to the contents of index register X to produce an address where data is either to be found or requires to be stored.

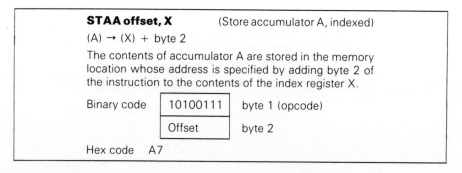

STAA offset, X   (Store accumulator A, indexed)

$(A) \rightarrow (X) + \text{byte 2}$

The contents of accumulator A are stored in the memory location whose address is specified by adding byte 2 of the instruction to the contents of the index register X.

Binary code | 10100111 | byte 1 (opcode)
| | Offset | byte 2

Hex code   A7

A hex code example

Byte 1	A7	Stores the contents of accumulator A
Byte 2	0F	in the memory location pointed to by the contents of the X register +15.

7.2.8   A sample program using immediate and indexed modes
The object of the following program is to load accumulator A with 02 (hex) and then store this binary pattern in 3 consecutive memory locations starting at A005.

Memory location	Hex code	Mnemonic	Comments
0000	86	LDAA	Load (immediate) accumulator A
0001	02	data	with 02 (hex).
0002	CE	LDX	Load (immediate) index register X
0003	A0	data	with A005 (hex).
0004	05		
0005	A7	STAA	Store (indexed) contents of accumulator A
0006	00	offset	in memory address (X) + 0 i.e. A005.
0007	A7	STAA	Store (indexed) contents of accumulator A
0008	01	offset	in memory address (X) + 1 i.e. A006.
0009	A7	STAA	Store (indexed) contents of accumulator A
000A	02	offset	in memory address (X) + 2 i.e. A007.

As a result of running the program, 02 (hex) will be stored in memory locations A005, A006 and A007.

Further machine code program examples for the 6802, using the full range of addressing modes, are given in Chapter 14.

7.3 The Intel 8085 addressing modes

The 8085 contains six 8-bit general-purpose working registers and an accumulator. The programmable registers are shown in Fig. 7.6. Each register has its own address, denoted by a 3-bit binary word DDD or SSS, as shown in Table 7.1.

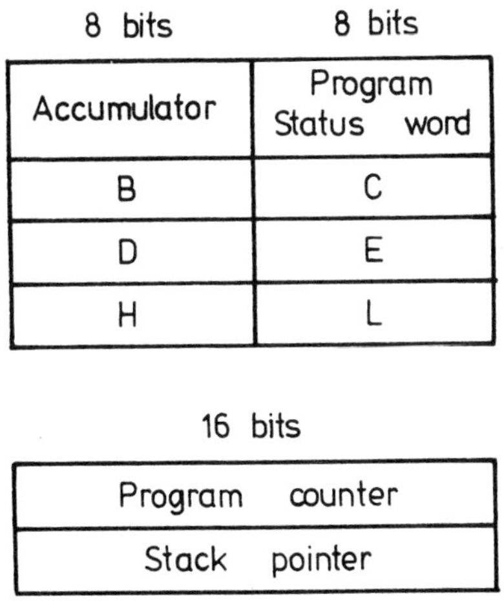

Fig. 7.6 8085 registers

Table 7.1 Intel 8085 programmable registers

DDD or SSS	Register name
111	Accumulator
000	B
001	C
010	D
011	E
100	H
101	L

In the addressing mode examples, if DDD is included in any instruction this indicates that the register selected is the 'destination' for any data movement. The use of SSS indicates that the register is the 'source' of any data movement.

Registers may be **paired** as follows:

1) B,C pair with B as the high-order register and C as the low-order register;
2) D,E pair with D as the high-order register and E as the low-order register;
3) H,L pair with H as the high-order register and L as the low-order register.

If the registers are paired in this way a new address, denoted by RP in Table 7.2, applies to the combination.

Table 7.2   Intel 8085 programmable register pairs

RP	Register pair
00	B,C
01	D,E
10	H,L
11	SP

7.3.1   Immediate mode

In this mode the instruction contains the data itself. This is either an 8-bit or a 16-bit quantity (least-significant byte first, most-significant byte second).

MVI r data   (Move immediate)

r ← byte 2

The content of byte 2 of the instruction is moved to register r.

Binary code	00DDD110	byte 1 (opcode)
	Data	byte 2

A hex code example

Byte 1	16	Loads register D
Byte 2	B5	with B5 (hex) (10110101 binary)

The opcode 16 is binary **000**10110 and so the DDD bits are 010, corresponding to register D.

7.3.2   Direct mode

Byte 2 and 3 of the instruction contain the exact memory address of the data item. The low-order-bits of the address are in byte 2, the high-order bits in byte 3.

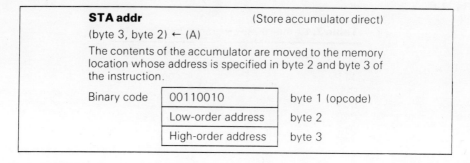

STA addr   (Store accumulator direct)

(byte 3, byte 2) ← (A)

The contents of the accumulator are moved to the memory location whose address is specified in byte 2 and byte 3 of the instruction.

Binary code	00110010	byte 1 (opcode)
	Low-order address	byte 2
	High-order address	byte 3

A hex code example

Byte 1	32	Stores the contents of the accumulator
Byte 2	C8	in location 1FC8.
Byte 3	1F	

7.3.3   A sample program using direct and immediate modes

The aim of the following program is to store respectively in memory locations ØDØ8 and ØD34 two specific binary patterns. One method of achieving this objective is to load the patterns initially into the accumulator.

Memory location	Hex code	Mnemonic	Comments
ØC70	3E	MVI A	Load (immediate) accumulator with
ØC71	Ø4	data	Ø4 (hex).
ØC72	32	STA	Store (direct) contents of
ØC73	Ø8 ⎫	address	accumulator in memory location
ØC74	ØD ⎭		ØDØ8.
ØC75	3E	MVI A	Load (immediate) accumulator with
ØC76	Ø3	data	Ø3 (hex).
ØC77	32	STA	Store (direct) contents of
ØC78	34 ⎫	address	accumulator in memory location
ØC79	ØD ⎭		ØD34.

Although the program is written into location ØC70 to ØC79, it could reside anywhere within the addressable memory space. However, due to certain characteristics of the 8085 CPU it is more usual for programs to be situated elsewhere than in the lower end of the memory space.

As a result of running this program, memory locations ØDØ8 will contain Ø4 (hex) and memory location ØD34 will contain Ø3 (hex).

7.3.4   Register mode

The instruction specifies the register or register pair in which the data is located. This mode allows operations on data within the CPU registers.

ADD r   (Add register)

A ← (A) + (r)

The content of register r is added to the content of the accumulator. The result is placed in the accumulator.

Binary code | 10000SSS | byte 1 (opcode)

A hex code example

Byte 1	8Ø	The content of register B is added to the content of the accumulator leaving the result in the accumulator.

The opcode 8Ø (hex) corresponds to binary **10000000**. The SSS bits are 000 which, from the list on page 65, specifies register B.

7.3.5   A sample program using immediate, direct and register modes

The following program is required to implement the mathematical equation $Z = Y + K$, where: Y is the value of variable data stored in memory location ØC40; K is a constant value equivalent to decimal 13 (expressed in binary that is 00001101 or ØD (hex); and Z is the result which will be stored in memory location ØC5B.

Memory location	Hex code	Mnemonic	Comments
ØC00	3E	MVI B	Load (immediate) register B
ØC01	ØD	data	with ØD (hex) i.e. constant K.
ØC02	3A	LDA	Load (direct) accumulator with
ØC03	40 ⎫	address	contents of memory location
ØC04	ØC ⎭		ØC40.
ØC05	80	ADD B	Add contents of accumulator to contents of register B, leaving result in accumulator.
ØC06	32	STA	Store (direct) accumulator contents
ØC07	5B ⎫	address	in memory location ØC5B
ØC08	ØC ⎭		
. . .			
ØC40	XX		Variable data (Y)
. . .			
ØC5B	XX		Result (Z)

After the program has been run, the result (Z) stored in memory location ØC5B will depend on the value of data (Y) that had previously been stored in ØC4A. As an example, if ØC4A contained 15 (hex) then result (Z) stored in ØC5B would be:

$$00001101 + 00010101 = 00100010$$

i.e.   22 (hex).

7.3.6   Register indirect mode

The instruction specifies a register pair which contains the memory address where the data is located. The high-order bits of the address are in the first register of the pair, the low-order bits in the second register.

LDAX RP	(Load accumulator indirect)
A ← ((RP))	

The contents of the memory location whose address is in register pair RP are moved to register A.

Binary code	00RP1010	byte 1 (opcode)

A hex code example

Byte 1	1A	The accumulator (register A) is loaded from a memory location whose address is held in register pair D,E.

The opcode 1A corresponds to binary 0001 1010. The register pair bits are 01, thus specifying register pair D,E.

Storing the contents of a register in a designated memory location can also be done by indirect addressing methods. The following instruction illustrates how this can be achieved.

STAX RP   (Store accumulator indirect)

(A) → ((RP))

The content of register A is moved to the memory location whose address is in the register pair RP.

Binary code | 00RP0010 | byte 1 (opcode)

A hex code example

Byte 1   02   The content of register A is stored in a
                            memory location whose address is specified
                            by the contents of register pair B,C.

The opcode 02 corresponds to binary 00000010. The register pair bits are 00, thus specifying register pair B,C.

7.3.7   A sample program using immediate, register, and register indirect modes
The aim of the following program is to load the accumulator with 02 (hex) and then store this binary pattern in 3 consecutive memory locations starting at A005.

Memory location	Hex code	Mnemonic	Comments
0C00	3E	MVI A	Load (immediate) accumulator
0C01	02	data	with 02 (hex).
0C02	01	LXI B	Load (immediate) register pair B,C
0C03	05	data	with A005 (hex).
0C04	A0		
0C05	02	STAX B	Store (indirect) the accumulator contents in the memory location pointed to by the contents of register pair B,C.
0C06	03	INX B	Increment contents of register pair B,C by 1.
0C07	02	STAX B	Store (indirect) the accumulator contents in the memory location pointed to by the contents of register pair B,C.
0C08	03	INX B	Increment contents of register pair B,C by 1.
0C09	02	STAX B	Store (indirect) the accumulator contents in the memory location pointed to by the contents of register pair B,C.

As a result of running the program, 02 (hex) will be stored in memory location A005, A006 and A007.

Further machine code program examples for the 8085, using the full range of addressing modes, are given in Chapter 14.

7.4   The MOS Technology 6502 addressing modes

The 6502 processor shares the same basic design philosophy as the 6800. However, as an enhancement it is not compatible. The instruction sets are entirely different, and there is a rearrangement of the programmable registers as shown in Fig. 7.7. There is only one primary accumulator and the index register is split into two 8-bit registers which may be used separately. One of these is called the X register, the other is denoted Y.

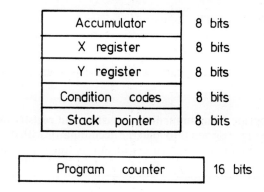

Fig. 7.7   6502 registers

7.4.1   Zero mode
This is a two-byte instruction, the first byte holding the opcode and the second specifying an address within the first 256 memory locations. Implementation is precisely the same as for the direct mode of the 6802, but in 6502 terminology this mode is referred to as **base page zero** addressing. This name is rooted in the idea that the memory may be separated into 'pages', each comprising 256 locations. Each page is numbered, with the lowest in the memory denoted by page 0 (zero) and successive pages numbering up from this.

7.4.2   Immediate mode
This is exactly the same as the 6802 immediate mode.

7.4.3   Absolute mode
The 6502 absolute mode is the same as the 6802 extended mode, in which the opcode is followed by a two-byte address. The only difference between the two implementations is that in the 6502 the second byte, which is the first address byte, provides the least significant half of the address.

7.4.4 The indexed mode

Significantly greater flexibility has been introduced in comparison with the 6802 indexed mode. The following four indexed modes are available, each using one or other of the two 8-bit X and Y index registers.

7.4.5 Base page indexed mode

In this two-byte instruction the second byte is the modifier which adds to the contents of the X register to indicate an address within the first 256 bytes of memory, i.e. within memory page zero. Should the sum be greater than 256 (FF hex) the carry is lost.

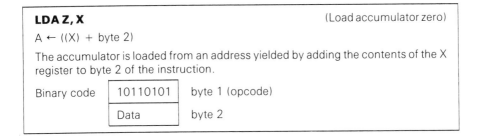

LDA Z, X (Load accumulator zero)

A ← ((X) + byte 2)

The accumulator is loaded from an address yielded by adding the contents of the X register to byte 2 of the instruction.

Binary code	10110101	byte 1 (opcode)
	Data	byte 2

A hex code example

Byte 1	B5	Loads the accumulator from
Byte 2	02	the address synthesised by adding 2 to the X register contents.

7.4.6 Pre-indexed indirect mode

The modifier in byte 2 adds to the contents of the X register to form an address within page zero. The page zero address plus the contents of the next location forms an address. The data resides in this final, indirectly arrived-at location.

Since the X or index register has only 8 bits this mode can reference addresses only in memory page zero, i.e. within the first 256 bytes. Only the X register can be used for this mode.

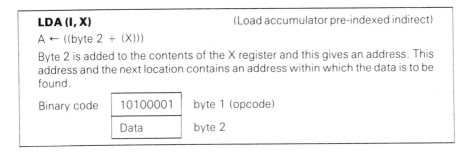

LDA (I, X) (Load accumulator pre-indexed indirect)

A ← ((byte 2 + (X)))

Byte 2 is added to the contents of the X register and this gives an address. This address and the next location contains an address within which the data is to be found.

Binary code	10100001	byte 1 (opcode)
	Data	byte 2

A hex code example

Byte 1	A1	Loads the accumulator from
Byte 2	05	an address synthesised by adding 5 to the X register contents to give an indirect address.

Assuming the X register contained 50 hex, the locations 0055 and 0056 would contain an address with four hex digits. This address holds the data and may be located anywhere within the 64 K total addressable space.

7.4.7 Post-indexed indirect mode

The modifier byte 2 refers to an address within memory base page zero. This location and the one which follows it hold an address with four hex digits. The contents of the Y register are added to this address to produce the final address of the data.

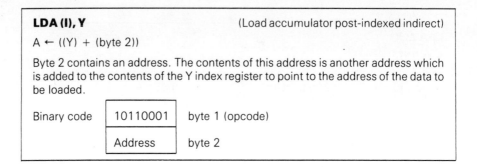

LDA (I), Y   (Load accumulator post-indexed indirect)

A ← ((Y) + (byte 2))

Byte 2 contains an address. The contents of this address is another address which is added to the contents of the Y index register to point to the address of the data to be loaded.

Binary code	10110001	byte 1 (opcode)
	Address	byte 2

A hex code example

Byte 1	B1	Loads the accumulator
Byte 2	07	from an address synthesised as follows.

The second byte, in this case 07, indicates address 0007. A two-byte address is held in locations 0007 and 0008. If the Y register holds 02, and assuming that 0007 and 0008 hold 0150, 02 is added to this to yield 0152, where the data resides. Only the Y register can be used in this mode of addressing.

7.4.8 Absolute indexed mode

In some respects this is the antithesis of the indexed mode of the 6802. Whereas in the 6802 an 8-bit modifier is added to a 16-bit index register to give the address, in the 6502 the content of one of the 8-bit index registers is added to a 16-bit address. This address is held in bytes 2 and 3, where byte 2 holds the least significant half of the address while byte 3 holds the most significant half.

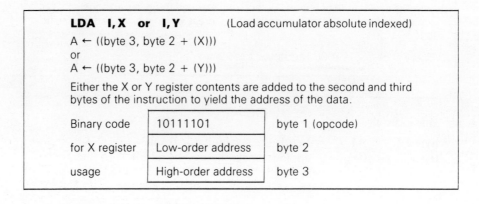

LDA I, X or I, Y   (Load accumulator absolute indexed)

A ← ((byte 3, byte 2 + (X)))

or

A ← ((byte 3, byte 2 + (Y)))

Either the X or Y register contents are added to the second and third bytes of the instruction to yield the address of the data.

Binary code	10111101	byte 1 (opcode)
for X register	Low-order address	byte 2
usage	High-order address	byte 3

A hex code example

Byte 1	BD	Loads the accumulator from
Byte 2	08	the address obtained by adding the contents of the
Byte 3	2A	X register to 2A08.

7.4.9   Implied mode

In this addressing mode the processor needs no more than the opcode to recognise and perform an operation on data that is already within the CPU. The implied mode corresponds to the inherent mode in the 6802. Additional inherent features are register-register transfers.

7.4.10   A sample program using the indexed modes and absolute mode

The object of the following program is to add together three numbers. The first is held in the address 00FF; the second is in 0250; and the third is in 0251. The result is stored in 0300. Additionally 50 must be put in location 0050 and 02 in 0051.

Memory address	Hex code	Mnemonic	Comments
0200	18	CLC	Clear carry bit.
0201	A0	LDY	Load Y register immediate
0202	04	data	with 04.
0203	A2	LDX	Load X register immediate
0204	FF	FF	with FF.
0205	B5	LDA, Z, X	Load accumulator
0206	00	data	base page indexed.
0207	A2	LDX	Load X register immediate
0208	00	data	with 00.
0209	61	ADC I, X	Add with carry accumulator and pre-indexed indirect address
020A	50	data	contents.
020B	18	CLC	Clear carry bit.
020C	91	STA, I, Y	Store accumulator in address
020D	50	data	post-indexed indirect.
020E	B9	LDA A, Y	Load accumulator from address
020F	4D	address	absolute indexed by Y.
0210	02		
0211	6D	ADC	Add with carry accumulator to
0212	54	address	contents of address (absolute).
0213	02		
0214	8D	STA	Store contents of accumulator
0215	00	address	in address extended direct.
0216	03		

7.5   The Zilog Z80 addressing modes

The programmable registers for the Zilog Z80 are shown in Fig. 7.8. In common with the 8085 there are general-purpose registers, but a complete extra set is provided. This alternative set includes an accumulator and flags register. The programmer has access only to the primary register set, but bidirectional transfer of the contents of A and A' is

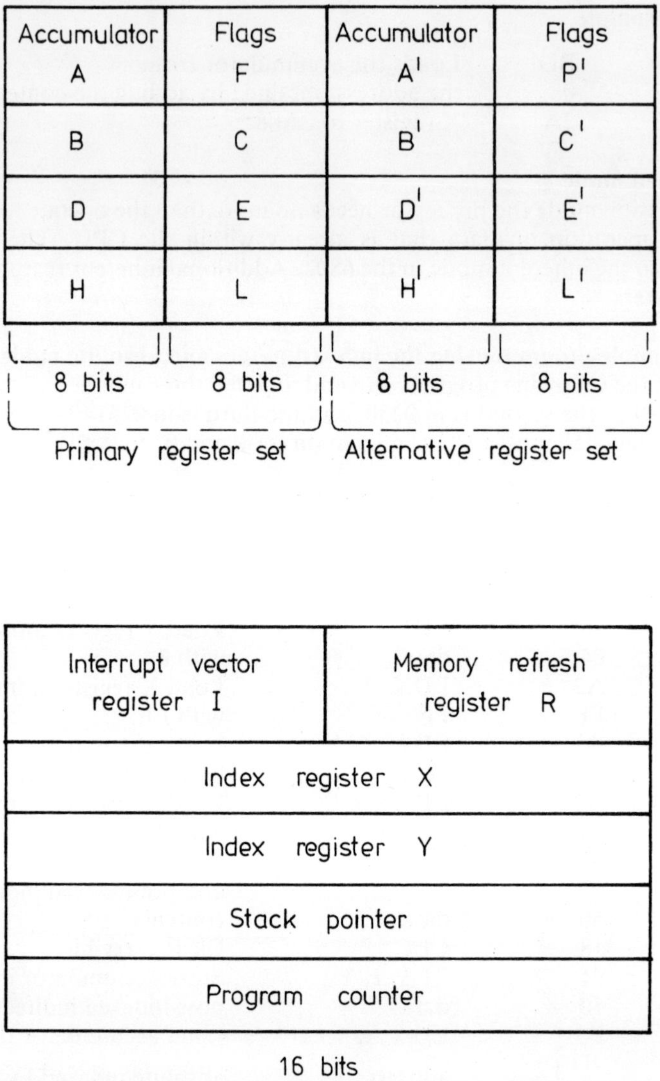

Accumulator A	Flags F	Accumulator A^I	Flags P^I
B	C	B^I	C^I
D	E	D^I	E^I
H	L	H^I	L^I

| 8 bits | 8 bits | 8 bits | 8 bits |
| Primary register set | | Alternative register set | |

Interrupt vector register I	Memory refresh register R
Index register X	
Index register Y	
Stack pointer	
Program counter	

16 bits

Fig. 7.8 Z80 registers

possible using a single instruction code. Similarly the contents of the flags registers F and P′ can be interchanged. Data transfer between the general-purpose registers B, C, D, E, H, L and B′, C′, D′, E′, H′, L′ can be achieved as a complete block move. Two 16-bit index registers and a 16-bit program counter are included as dedicated registers.

7.5.1   Register indirect, immediate, register and direct modes
The Z80 possesses immediate, direct, register indirect, and register modes precisely as implemented in the 8085. The opcodes for these are the same, so that programs written for the 8085 will run on the Z80 provided that the rest of the system is compatible; for instance, the memory must be located similarly.

7.5.2   The indexed mode

Byte 3 of the instruction is a modifier or displacement which can be added to either the X or Y register. Either register may be referred to, and the modifier can add to or subtract from the register contents by using a 2's complement number to specify a location. Since only one modifier byte is used, the range of reference is +127 to −128. Some of the instructions in the Z80 set are two-byte opcodes, and the indexed mode is in this class.

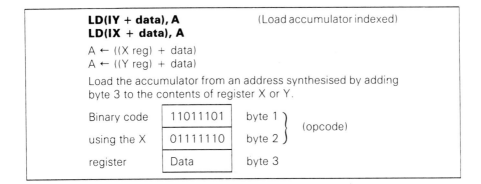

A hex code example

Byte 1	DD	Loads the accumulator from
Byte 2	7E	an address pointed to by
Byte 3	Ø7	the contents of the X register +7.

If the X register contains FEØØ the data will be fetched from FEØ7.

7.5.3   A sample program using immediate and indexed modes

In the following program, the X register is loaded with ØDØØ, and the Y register with ØD1Ø. The accumulator is loaded with FE. The X register is then incremented to hold ØDØ1 and the content is added to the accumulator before the result in the accumulator is stored in ØD1Ø.

Memory location	Hex code	Mnemonic	Comments
ØC70	DD ⎫	LDIX	Load X immediate
ØC71	21 ⎭		extended with
ØC72	ØØ ⎫	address	ØDØØ.
ØC73	ØD ⎭		
ØC74	FD ⎫	LDIY	Load Y immediate
ØC75	21 ⎭		extended with
ØC76	1Ø ⎫	address	ØD1Ø.
ØC77	ØD ⎭		
ØC78	3E	LD, A	Load the accumulator
ØC79	FE	data	with FE.

(continued overleaf)

Memory location	Hex code	Mnemonic	Comments
ØC7A	DD	INC, IX	Increment X.
ØC7B	23		
ØC7C	DD	ADD, (IX + d)	Add to accumulator the contents
ØC7D	86		of the location pointed to by X.
ØC7E	ØØ		
ØC7F	FD	LD, IY, r	Store accumulator in
ØC8Ø	77		address pointed to
ØC81	ØØ		by Y.
ØC82	76		Halt.

8
Jumping, branching and subroutines

All microprocessors have a **program counter** which contains the address of the next instruction to be executed. Normally, consecutive lines of a program are stored in consecutive memory locations, and so to run a program it is only necessary to increment the program counter by one each time the processor fetches an opcode or data.

The exception to this sequential action is when a **jump** or **branch** instruction is detected. Executing this type of instruction can cause the microprocessor to go anywhere in memory to obtain the next instruction opcode. The terms 'jumping' and 'branching' can initially be thought of as synonymous actions. However, in certain commercial products a distinction is made between jump and branch operations.

Two fundamental types of jump or branch instruction exist. These are:

i)   unconditional jumping/branching;
ii) conditional jumping/branching.

8.1 Unconditional jump instructions

The concept of an unconditional jump instruction is that execution of the main program should stop on receipt of the jump command, and begin again at a specified address which can be anywhere within the addressable memory space. In order to achieve this, the program counter must be loaded with the address to be jumped to. In the simplest case, the jump instruction itself contains the 16-bit address (see Fig. 8.1).

When the CPU finishes the fetch cycle of a jump instruction, the program counter is already pointing to the memory location containing the opcode of the next instruction (see Section 6.3). This is stage 1 in Fig. 8.1. On executing the jump operation the program counter is loaded with bytes 2 and 3 of the instruction (stage 2). The program counter now automatically points to a new memory address (stage 3) and will carry out a fetch cycle on the opcode of the instruction stored there. The old information contained in the program counter is now lost and there is no way the program can return to its original place, other than by a second unconditional jump instruction.

A specific example of the steps involved when implementing an unconditional jump instruction is shown in Fig. 8.2.

The CPU fetches the 3-byte instruction stored in memory locations 0205, 0206 and 0207. At the completion of the three fetch cycles the CPU will know from the opcode that it will be carrying out a jump operation and also the memory address to jump to — 034A (hex). However, before executing the current instruction, the program counter will increment to 0208 (step 1 in Fig. 8.2). At this stage, the contents of the program counter are not brought out onto the address bus but are ready to point to the position of the next sequential instruction, if required. The execution of the jump instruction causes the 16-bit address 034A to be loaded into the program counter. This is shown as step 2 in Fig. 8.2. The CPU is now pointing to a different area of memory where it commences a new fetch cycle on the contents of memory location 034A. It must always be arranged that an opcode resides at this location for a correct fetch-execute cycle to be

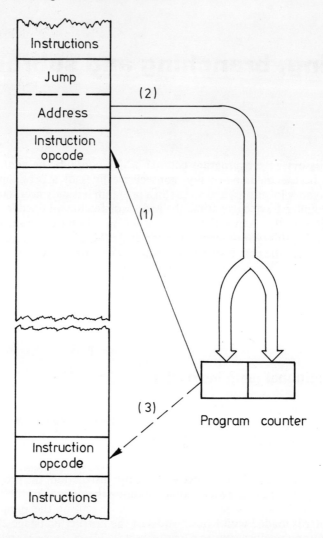

Fig. 8.1 An unconditional jump

implemented. As the old contents of the program counter (Ø2Ø8) have been over-written the CPU will not return to that area of the program unless instructed at a later stage to do so.

8.2   Conditional jump instructions

Conditional jump instructions allow jumps in the program operation to occur only when certain specified conditions exist. Deciding on whether these conditions are present is made possible by examining status flags in the CPU which keep track of arithmetic and logic operations. These flags automatically set and reset as instructions are being executed and normally indicate the current status or condition of the accumulator contents. A typical group of status flags was shown in Fig. 4.4 where the condition of the Z,N,P and O flags could be used to determine whether the arithmetic result of executing an immediately previous instruction was: zero, negative, positive or had overflowed (number too large to handle).

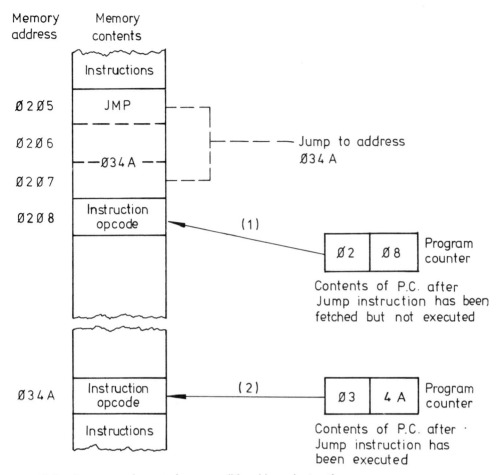

Fig. 8.2 Sequence of events for unconditional jump instruction

All conditional jump instructions go through a similar sequence of operations to decide whether a jump should take place. A typical sequence is as follows.

1) CPU decodes the conditional jump instruction opcode.
2) CPU checks the condition of the specified flag or flags. These may have been changed as a result of a previous instruction.
3) If condition is true the program counter is set to a new value which specifies the memory location the program should jump to.
4) If condition is not true the CPU implements a fetch-execute cycle on the next instruction in the program sequence.

Figure 8.3 shows an example of a program flow where conditional jump instructions are present. In the case of the first conditional jump instruction of Fig. 8.3, the CPU flag that indicates whether the accumulator contents are positive would be examined. If the flag is set then a jump to a specified address would occur, otherwise the program would continue in its normal sequence. The other conditional jump takes place if the accumulator contents are zero. Here again the CPU zero flag would automatically set when the accumulator contents were zero, and by examining this flag a decision can be made as to whether a jump to a specified address takes place. If this is not the case the

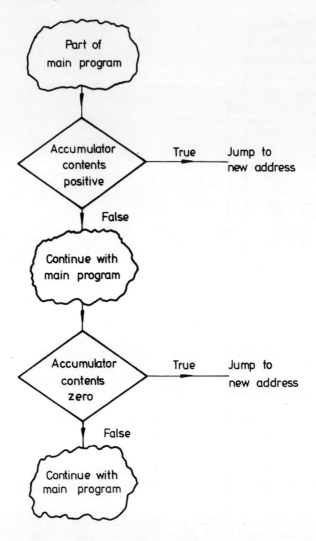

Fig. 8.3   Program flow with conditional jumps

CPU fetches and executes the next instruction stored after the conditional jump instruction.

   A more detailed example of the status flags and program counter operation is shown in Fig. 8.4(a) and Fig. 8.4(b).

   Not all instructions are of the type that will cause the status flags to change, but if it is assumed that implementing the LDA instruction (load accumulator with the contents of a memory location) causes the status flags to take up an appropriate state, then the following situations could occur.

   i)   If the accumulator was loaded with a positive number the P flag would set, otherwise it would remain in a reset condition.
   ii) If the accumulator was loaded with a negative number the N flag would set, otherwise it would remain in a reset condition.

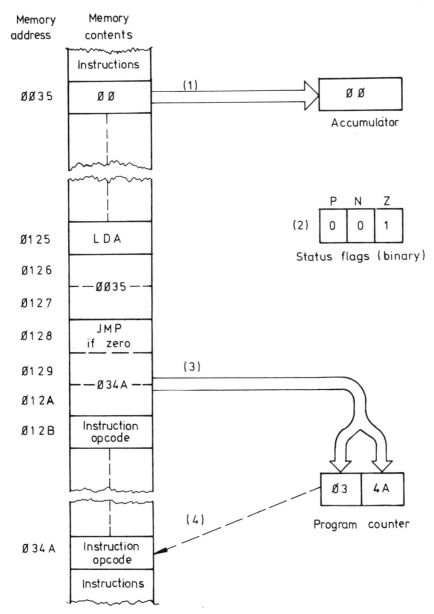

Fig. 8.4 (a) Conditional jump instruction true

iii) If the accumulator was loaded with a zero the Z flag would set, otherwise it would remain in a reset condition.

In Fig. 8.4(a) the LDA instruction causes the data 00 (hex) to be loaded from memory location 0035 into the accumulator (step 1). This automatically sets the Z flag (step 2). On executing the JMP If Zero instruction, the Z flag is examined. As it is set, 034A is loaded into the program counter (step 3) and the program sequence now jumps to this area of memory for the next instruction (step 4).

In Fig. 8.4(b) the LDA instruction causes the data 08 (hex) to be loaded from memory location 0035 into the accumulator. Under these conditions the Z flag remains reset and

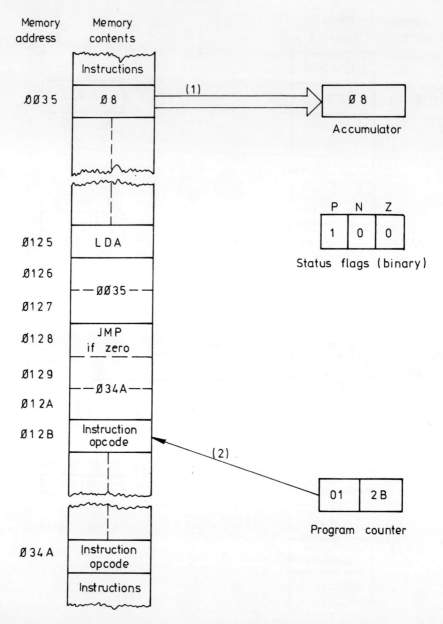

Fig. 8.4 (b) Conditional jump instruction false

therefore on executing the JMP If Zero instruction, no jump takes place and the CPU fetches and executes the next instructions pointed to by the program counter — the instruction stored at Ø12B.

8.3 Subroutines

In programming there can be instances where program segments are repetitive, but it is wasteful of memory to store the same blocks of instructions at different points in the program. A more efficient scheme is to create within the program an area which can be re-entered as many times as is necessary. This area may contain any number of instructions, and after they have been executed each time the processor must jump back to the main stream of the program and continue. Such an area is called a **subroutine**. There are special instruction codes which cause the processor to jump to a subroutine, and to return from it; see Fig. 8.5. The use of subroutines can shorten programs considerably, but this advantage is offset to some extent because special operations by the CPU are required, and this slows down program execution. These delays are concerned with the operation of the stack.

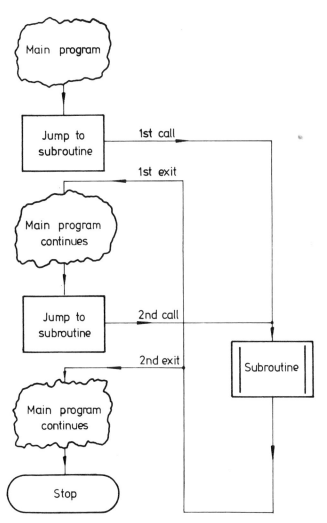

Fig. 8.5   Flowchart involving a subroutine

8.4   The stack

When the processor encounters a jump instruction the program counter is loaded with the address to be jumped to. However, when the jump is to a subroutine, the requirement is that after the subroutine execution is complete the processor must return to take up where it left off in the main program. This necessitates saving the state of the program counter in memory and reinstating it on demand. The area in memory allocated for this temporary storage function is called the stack and is pointed to by the address in the stack pointer register (SP). As each item of information is stored in the memory location addressed by the stack pointer, the contents of the stack pointer are decremented by one. Now a new memory location within the stack area is being pointed to. This operation is called **pushing the stack**. When a subroutine jump is ordered the following events take place, as illustrated in Fig. 8.6.

1)   The least significant byte of the program counter is stored in the address pointed to by the contents of the stack pointer register.
2)   The stack pointer register is decremented by one, and the most significant byte of the program counter is stored in the next location (SP −1).
3)   The program counter is loaded with the address of the subroutine.
4)   Subroutine execution commences.

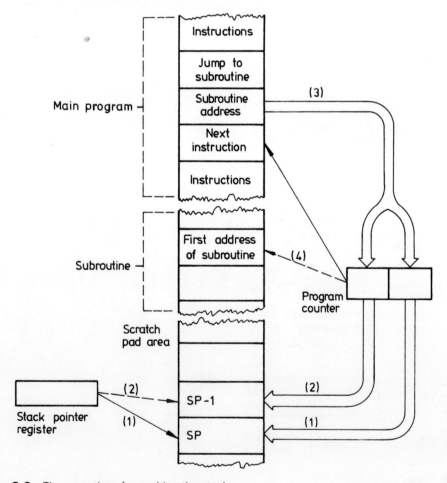

Fig. 8.6   The operations for pushing the stack

When a 'return from subroutine' instruction is encountered the reverse sequence of operations must take place and this is called **pulling** or **popping** the stack. The steps required are as follows, and are illustrated in Fig. 8.7.

1) The contents of the store address pointed to by the stack pointer register are loaded into the most significant part of the program counter.
2) The stack pointer register is incremented by one and the contents of the store pointed to by the stack pointer register are loaded into the least significant part of the program counter register.
3) Main program execution recommences.

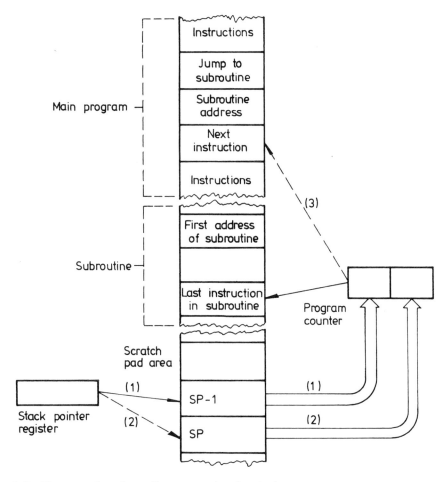

Fig. 8.7   The operations for pulling or popping the stack

A more detailed examination of the operations required to implement a subroutine is shown in Fig. 8.8. After fetching the 3-byte instruction at 0205, 0206 and 0207 the CPU will know that it is required to jump to a subroutine starting at memory location 034A. However, before this action is carried out the present contents of the program counter, which indicate the location of the next instruction in the main program, will have to be stored on the stack. Therefore, the first steps involved are as follows.

1) 08 (hex) is stored in memory location 0508.

2) Stack pointer register decremented by one and Ø2 (hex) stored in Ø5Ø7. Now that the return address of the main program has been stored on the stack, a jump to subroutine can take place.
3) Subroutine address Ø34A is loaded into the program counter and CPU now looks to memory address Ø34A as the location with the next instruction opcode to fetch and execute.

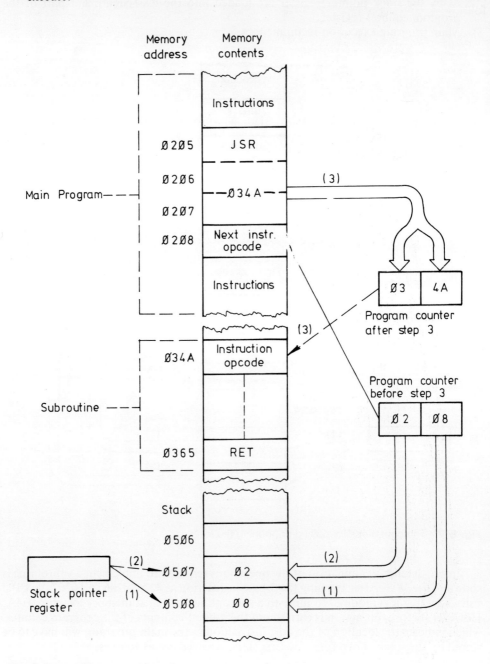

Fig. 8.8   Jumping to a subroutine

The microprocessor has now jumped to the subroutine and will continue to fetch and execute instruction from memory location Ø34A onwards. This process will continue until it is required to execute the special return from subroutine RET instruction.

The detailed sequence of events which takes place on returning from a subroutine is shown in Fig. 8.9. After fetching the RET instruction the program counter is incremented to Ø366, though this of no importance with regard to the sequence of events that follows. Executing the RET instruction causes the contents of the memory location

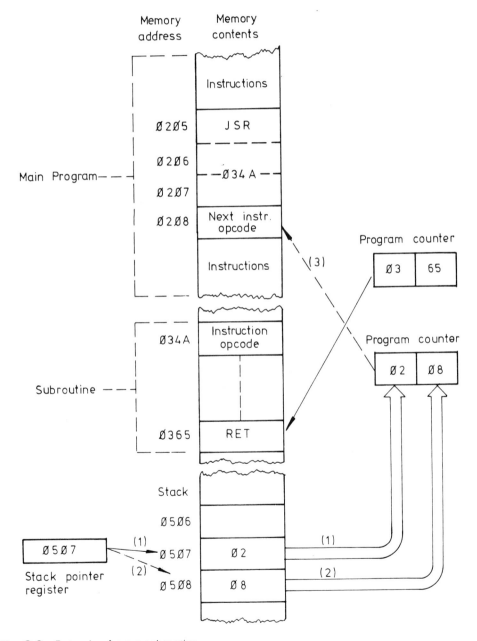

Fig. 8.9 Returning from a subroutine

pointed to by the stack pointer register to be transferred to the program counter as follows.

1)   Ø2 (hex) is transferred to most significant bits of program counter.
2)   Stack pointer register is incremented by one to Ø5Ø8 and Ø8 (hex) is transferred to least significant bits of program counter.

The program counter is now pointing to the memory address Ø2Ø8 as the next location to fetch and execute on instruction from. This is perfectly correct and completes the orderly jump and return from a subroutine.

The nesting of subroutines
If, during the execution of a subroutine, another subroutine call is encountered, then the contents of the program counter are again pushed onto the stack. This does not create any problems since the stack pointer register will be further decremented to accommodate the address within the first subroutine to be returned to at the completion of the second subroutine. The limiting factor in the number of times that this process can be invoked is the size of the memory allocated to the stack. Each time a subroutine is called within another it is said that a **level** of call is added.

Every subroutine must terminate in the instruction which pulls the return address off the stack. This results in a series of events organised as in Table 8.1, where it should be noted that the 'call' and 'return' commands for the three levels of call are nested one inside the other.

Table 8.1

Step number	Event
1	Call subroutine 1 resident at Ø34A; push stack.
2	During this subroutine, call subroutine 2 resident at Ø286; push stack.
3	During this subroutine, call subroutine 3 resident at Ø4AF; push stack. Do subroutine 3.
4	Return from subroutine 3; pull stack Continue with subroutine 2.
5	Return from subroutine 2; pull stack Continue with subroutine 1.
6	Return from subroutine 1; pull stack.

The mechanism of the push stack operation is illustrated in Fig. 8.10. The process of pulling the stack requires the reverse procedure.

8.5   Jumping, branching and subroutines in the 6802

The 6802 has two instruction codes for unconditional jumping; one uses the extended mode, the other the indexed mode.

It also has a modified form of unconditional jumping called a **branch** instruction. All branch instructions are two bytes long, and the second byte is a 2's complement binary number which refers to the number of memory locations that are to be jumped over, either forward or backward, from the current address in the program counter. The jump destination is thus indicated relative to the program counter contents; jumps of this type are called branches.

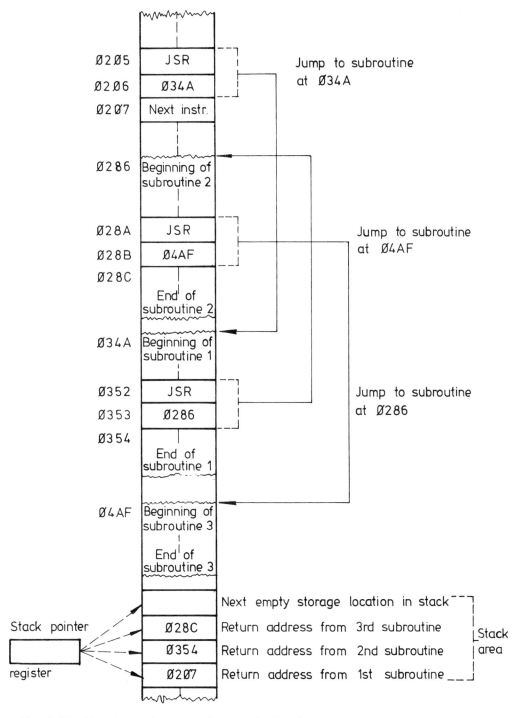

Fig. 8.10   How the stack operates for nested subroutines

8.5.1   Unconditional jumping

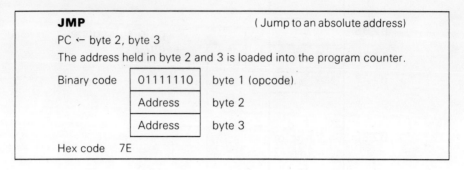

```
JMP                                    ( Jump to an absolute address)
PC ← byte 2, byte 3
The address held in byte 2 and 3 is loaded into the program counter.

Binary code    | 01111110 |   byte 1 (opcode)
               | Address  |   byte 2
               | Address  |   byte 3

Hex code    7E
```

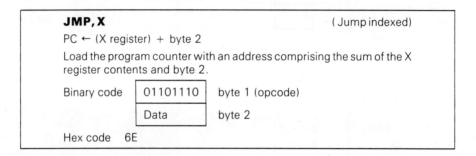

```
JMP, X                                 ( Jump indexed)
PC ← (X register) + byte 2
Load the program counter with an address comprising the sum of the X
register contents and byte 2.

Binary code    | 01101110 |   byte 1 (opcode)
               | Data     |   byte 2

Hex code    6E
```

8.5.2   Unconditional branching
There is one unconditional branch instruction, described as **branch always**.

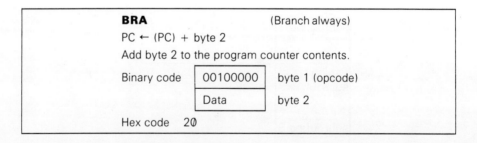

```
BRA                                    (Branch always)
PC ← (PC) + byte 2
Add byte 2 to the program counter contents.

Binary code    | 00100000 |   byte 1 (opcode)
               | Data     |   byte 2

Hex code    20
```

The program counter contents always point to the next instruction to be executed. This must be remembered when programming, because a forward branch of three places will have a destination that is five locations ahead of the branch command; see Fig. 8.11.

When a backward branch is required the second byte must be expressed as a 2's complement number. It must be borne in mind that a backward jump of five places will actually be to a destination that is three locations before the opcode; see Fig. 8.12.

8.5.3   Conditional branching
There are a large number of 'branch on condition' instructions. These initiate tests on the **flags register**, which is also called the **condition codes register** (CCR). The tests check individual bits within the register to see whether or not a particular condition exists.

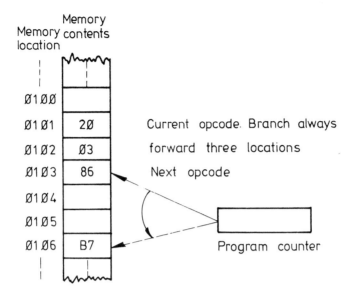

Fig. 8.11   A forward relative branch

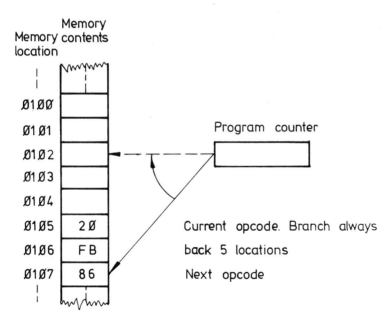

Fig. 8.12   A backward relative branch

The 6802 condition codes register

b7	b6	b5	b4	b3	b2	b1	bØ
1	1	H	I	N	Z	V	C

Fig. 8.13 The 6802 condition codes register

Figure 8.13 shows the condition codes register. The purpose of each bit is described below. Bits 7 and 6 are permanently 'set' because they are not used.

b5–H The half carry flag H is set when an arithmetic operation causes a carry to occur from b3 to b4 of the data word in the accumulator.

b4–I The interrupt mask bit I is set if an interrupt is being serviced. This ensures that no further interrupt can be effected whilst the first is being dealt with. This is discussed further in Chapter 9.

b3–N The sign bit N is set if an arithmetic operation produces a negative result in the accumulator.

b2–Z This bit is set if the result of an arithmetic or logic function is zero.

b1–V If there is an arithmetic overflow in the accumulator, the overflow bit V signals the fact.

bØ–C This bit is set if an arithmetic operation generates a carry from the most significant bit (b7) of the resultant data word in the accumulator.

8.5.4 Using the condition codes register
Consider opcode 2B — branch if minus. Bit 3(N) of the flags register is checked; if N is set the jump takes place, otherwise it does not (see Fig. 8.14). In opcode 26 — branch if not equal to zero — bit 2 (Z) is checked. This time, if Z is set, the branch does not take place.

Many conditional instructions carry out tests on several flags.

8.5.5 Branching and jumping to subroutines
The 'jump to subroutine' instruction is of course unconditional, but when executed it pushes the current program counter contents onto the stack. This action does not take place in the other unconditional jump conditions.

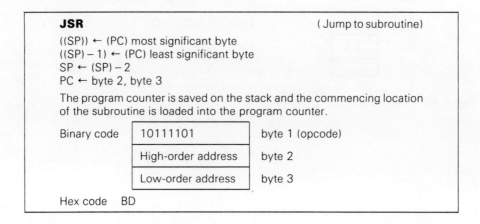

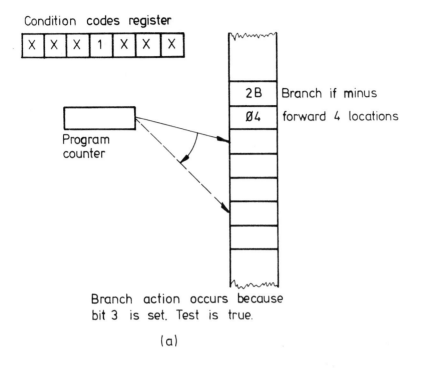

Branch action occurs because
bit 3 is set. Test is true.

(a)

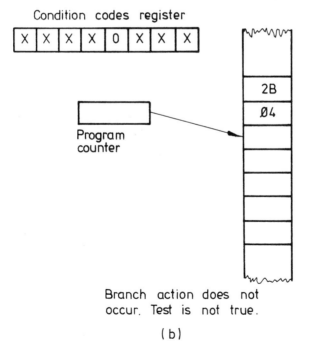

Branch action does not
occur. Test is not true.

(b)

Fig. 8.14   Relative branch action

Jumping to a subroutine implies that an absolute address is provided, so that the opcode is followed by two bytes of address. It is possible to branch to subroutine using the program counter relative jump, in which case only one byte follows the opcode. Whatever method is used, the subroutine entered must terminate with a 'return from subroutine' instruction.

RTS (Return from subroutine)

PC least significant byte ← ((SP))
SP ← (SP) +1
PC most significant byte ← ((SP))
SP ← (SP) +1

The address of the next byte to be executed in the main program is pulled off the stack and the main program continues.

Binary code   00111001   byte 1

Hex code   39

The use of subroutine operations is probably best described with the aid of an example.

8.5.6   An example using jump and branch instructions

A subroutine technique and conditional branching instruction could be used in a search routine. Assume that for some reason it is necessary to run through memory looking for certain data, say hex code 04. Furthermore, the contents of each location should be output to a display as an ASCII character until when 04 is encountered the program stops. In the example both jump and branch to subroutine are used; each operation is associated with a different subroutine. The subroutine resident at location E1D1 (hex) is assumed to use the contents of the accumulator to output an ASCII character to the display. The characters to be printed are resident in locations from 0150 upwards. It must be remembered that the routine beginning at E1D1 (hex) will terminate with the RTS instruction 39 (hex), therefore the RTS instruction at 0017 refers to the subroutine call at 0009. Figure 8.15 is a flowchart for this program, which is listed on pp. 95 and 97.

Memory location	Hex code	Mnemonic	Comments
0000	CE	LDX	Load X register immediate
0001	01	address	with 0150.
0002	50		
0003	A6	LDAA, X	Load the accumulator.
0004	00	data	
0005	81	CMP, A	Compare accumulator contents
0006	04	data	immediate with 04.
0007	27	BEQ	Branch if equal forward
0008	04	data	four places (to 000D).
0009	8D	BSR	Branch to subroutine located
000A	08	data	forward eight locations (at 0013).
000B	20	BRA	Branch always back ten
000C	F6	data	locations (to 0003).

(continued on page 96)

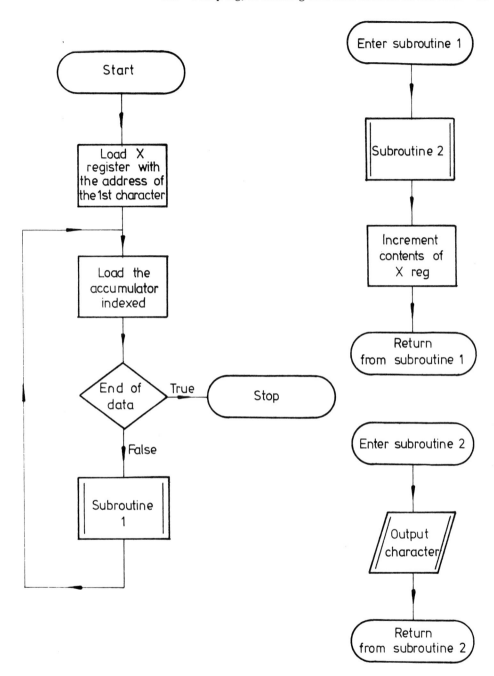

Fig. 8.15 A flowchart for the example program using subroutines and conditional branching

Memory location	Hex code	Mnemonic	Comments
000D	7E	JMP	Jump unconditionally to
000E	**	address	a 'halt' instruction.
000F	**		
:			
0013	BD	JSR	Jump to subroutine
0014	E1	address	resident at E1D1.
0015	D1		
0016	08	INX	Increment the contents of X.
0017	39	RTS	Return from subroutine (to 000B).

8.6 Jumping and subroutines in the 8085

8.6.1 Unconditional jumping
The 8085 has three main unconditional jump instructions, but no relative branching. The three instructions are as follows:

i)   JMP — jump
ii) CALL — jump to subroutine
iii) RST — restart

8.6.2 The JMP instruction
Execution of this three-byte instruction simply causes the program counter to jump to the address specified in the second and third bytes of the instruction.

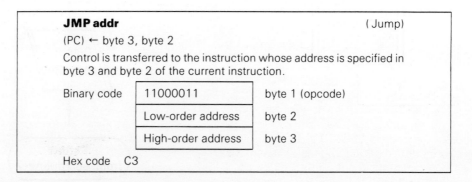

8.6.3 The CALL instruction
This is a special type of jump instruction which causes the program counter to jump to a memory address where the start of a subroutine is stored. After the processor has finished with the last instruction in the subroutine a return to the main program must be initiated. In the 8085 this is achieved by placing a RET instruction at the end of the subroutine.

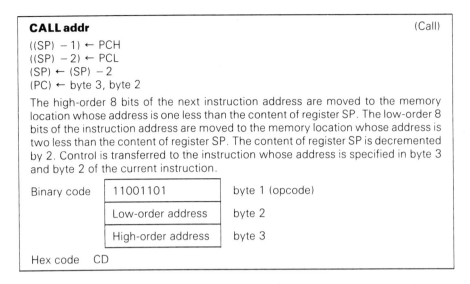

CALL addr   (Call)

((SP) − 1) ← PCH
((SP) − 2) ← PCL
(SP) ← (SP) − 2
(PC) ← byte 3, byte 2

The high-order 8 bits of the next instruction address are moved to the memory
location whose address is one less than the content of register SP. The low-order 8
bits of the instruction address are moved to the memory location whose address is
two less than the content of register SP. The content of register SP is decremented
by 2. Control is transferred to the instruction whose address is specified in byte 3
and byte 2 of the current instruction.

Binary code	11001101	byte 1 (opcode)
	Low-order address	byte 2
	High-order address	byte 3

Hex code   CD

8.6.4   The RST instruction

This one-byte special unconditional jump instruction can be used for calling subroutines
resident at specific places in memory. The programmer can choose any of eight RST
instructions which will cause the present contents of the program counter to be pushed
onto the stack and one of the locations given in Table 8.2 to be loaded into the program
counter.

Table 8.2   RST instructions for the 8085

RST instruction	Hex code	Subroutine address (hex)
RST0	C7	0000
RST1	CF	0008
RST2	D7	0010
RST3	DF	0018
RST4	E7	0020
RST5	EF	0028
RST6	F7	0030
RST7	FF	0038

This means that the code C7 calls a subroutine beginning at location 0000 and that
each of the other RST codes calls subroutines located as listed.

By including a JMP instruction in one of these locations it is possible for the main
body of the subroutine to be held in other areas of the memory starting at the address
included in bytes 2 and 3 of the JMP instruction.

On completing the subroutine, inclusion of the instruction RET causes the top address
on the stack to be popped into the program counter. The main program will now
continue at the instruction in memory immediately following the location where the RST
instruction was stored.

8.6.5   Conditional jumping

On execution of a conditional jump instruction the status of one of the four condition
flags is examined to determine whether or not a specified jump should take place.

The four condition flags available in the CPU are: zero (Z), sign (S), parity (P), and carry (CY). These flags are either reset or set depending on the result of executing a specific instruction. Table 8.3 shows the conditions that may be checked in order to make a decision whether or not to jump.

Table 8.3   Conditions for conditional jumping in the 8085

Condition	Flag state	Binary condition code (CCC)
Not zero	Z = 0	000
Zero	Z = 1	001
No carry	C = 0	010
Carry	C = 1	011
Parity odd	P = 0	100
Parity even	P = 1	101
Sign plus	S = 0	110
Sign minus	S = 1	111

A fifth processor flag called the **auxiliary carry** is included in the CPU; however, this flag is not used for conditional jumping.

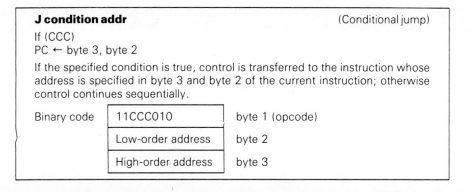

The appropriate jump opcode is made up to include as bits 5, 4 and 3 the binary condition code from the list of flags register possible states. Bits 7, 6 and 1 are always set, but bits 0 and 2 are reset in this class of instruction. Suppose that a test for an accumulator result equal to zero was required. The binary condition code for this is 001. By substituting this code into bits 5, 4 and 3 the opcode 11001010 (binary), CA hex, is formed. If it were required to test for a negative result the condition code 111 would be used, producing an opcode of 11111010, FA hex. Figure 8.16 demonstrates the action of conditional jump instructions by dealing with 'jump if equal to zero'.

The 8085 has provision for a conditional call as well as a conditional return from a subroutine. The H,L register pair also provides a basis for an indirect jump.

8.6.6   Indirect jumping

This is an unconditional jump in which the contents of the H,L register pair are moved into the program counter. The address where program execution is to recommence must therefore be placed in the H,L registers.

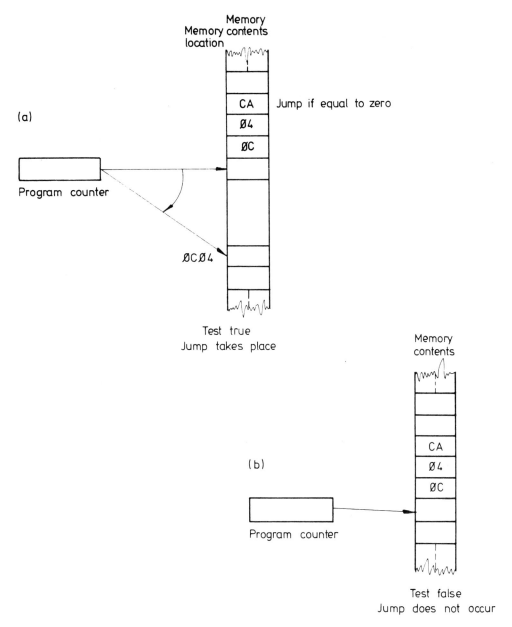

Fig. 8.16 Relative conditional jump action

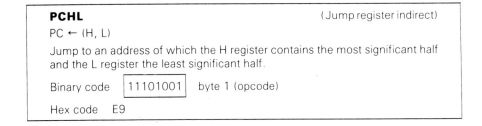

8.6.7 An example program using jump and call instructions

The following program demonstrates how 8085 instructions could perform the function indicated in the flowchart of Fig. 8.15. The subroutine at Ø13B is assumed to output an ASCII character to the display; the message is held in location ØD5Ø upwards. The routine beginning at Ø13B will be terminated by a return from subroutine command. The main program will therefore recommence at ØD11, thereafter returning to ØD09 if the character in the accumulator is not Ø4.

Memory location	Hex code	Mnemonic	Comments
ØDØØ	Ø6	MVI B	Load the B register
ØDØ1	Ø4	data	with hex Ø4.
ØDØ2	21	LXI H	Load the H,L register pair
ØDØ3	5Ø	} address	with the first address of
ØDØ4	ØD		data.
ØDØ5	7E	MOV A	Load the accumulator from ØD5Ø.
ØDØ6	CD	CALL	Jump to the subroutine
ØDØ7	ØD	} address	at ØDØD.
ØDØ8	ØD		
ØDØ9	23	INX H	Increment the H,L pair.
ØDØA	C3	JMP	Jump unconditionally to
ØDØB	Ø5	} address	ØDØ5.
ØDØC	ØD		
ØDØD	B8	CMP B	Compare registers A accumulator and B.
ØDØE	C4	CNZ	Jump if not equal to subroutine
ØDØF	3B	} address	at Ø13B.
ØD1Ø	Ø1		
ØD11	CØ	RNZ	Return if not equal.
ØD12	E1		Pop stack.
ØD13	76	HLT	Halt processor operation.

8.7 Jumping, branching and subroutines in the Z80

Unconditional and conditional jumps are precisely the same as the 8085 implementation, even using the same opcodes. Another area of similarity is in the conditional call series of instructions.

Indirect jumps, however, are expanded in that both the index registers X and Y can be used as well as the H,L pair to perform an indirect jump operation. The use of the RST (restart) group of commands is identical, but the Z80 allows program counter relative jumping, i.e. branching.

8.7.1 Conditional branching

Depending upon the outcome of a test of the condition flags a jump may be made to a location that is within a limited range of the currently executed opcode. The range is -128 to $+127$ locations, and byte 2 of the instruction represents the modifier or displacement to be added to the program counter contents. As in other processors a backward jump is achieved by adding a 2's complement modifier.

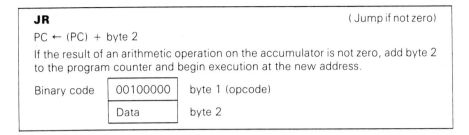

A very useful innovation in the Z80 is the opcode allowing register B to be decremented and tested; if it does not contain zero a relative jump occurs. For example, in programs in which a subroutine is to be executed a certain number of times, register B can act as a counter. The decrement and test feature would then result in a shorter and more efficient routine.

8.8   Jumping, branching and subroutines in the 6502

The principles used for conditional branching are those of the 6800 family, but a reduced number of tests are available for conditional operations. The absolute jump is also as used in the 6802, but in addition an indirect jump is available.

8.8.1   Indirect jumps

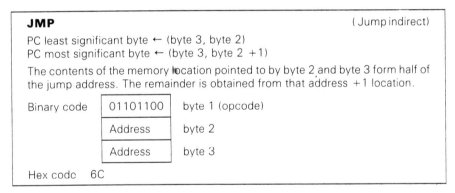

8.8.2   Subroutines
The stack pointer register in the 6502 has only 8 bits and as a result can only be loaded with 00 to FF (hex). This is only half of a four hex digit address, and the most significant half always defaults to 01. The stack can therefore be implemented only between 0100 and 01FF. Systems using this processor must organise this memory area as a scratchpad, not normally available for program space, unless the resultant restrictions on levels of call in subroutines are accepted. A scratchpad memory is used by the processor to jot down important data to be reclaimed later. In this case the data is the address from which sequential program execution is to recommence after a subroutine has been completed.

9

Input/output data transfer methods

Whatever the application, a microprocessor system must be able to accept data from an input peripheral device and transfer data processed within the CPU to an output peripheral. These input/output data transfer movements will always require inter-related hardware and software facilities.

Firstly the hardware facility. This allows the microprocessor system to be interfaced to the outside world. As an interface is the line dividing two zones operating under different conditions, interfacing is therefore a matching function. In a complete microprocessor system the hardware matching is carried out by the input/output (interface) device. This unit connects the microprocessor system to the world of the peripheral, and accordingly organises the data transferred to and from the peripheral device so that it may be assimilated by the computer system. Generally the input/output device is connected to the microprocessor via the address, data and control busses. Suitable decoding on the address bus will make the device appear as a memory location. This is referred to as a 'memory mapping' input/output technique. Chapter 10 will examine certain types of input/output devices in more detail, but for the present, the simple block diagram shown in Fig. 9.1 will be adequate.

The interface unit has both an input and an output port. These ports are made up of data storage registers that hold the information being transferred to or from the peripheral device. The register on the input port will need to have a tristate output as it is connected to the microcomputer system data bus. The reason for this type of tristate connection was discussed in Section 4.4. As the ports are memory mapped each port has its own address which is determined by the address decoding logic.

Once the hardware interface facilities have been established, all data transfer operations will take place under software control. The instructions that are suitable for this purpose are the same set as used for transferring data in and out of memory. The reason for this is that the data registers in the interface effectively appear as memory locations.

An example of a simple software program for transferring data from the accumulator of the CPU to an output peripheral device would be:

Mnemonic	Comments
LDA data	Load accumulator with data to be transferred to the output.
STA address address	Store contents of accumulator in the output port data register selected by the 16-bit address.

Alternatively the reading of any data from an input peripheral via an interface device can be accomplished by using the following software instruction sequence:

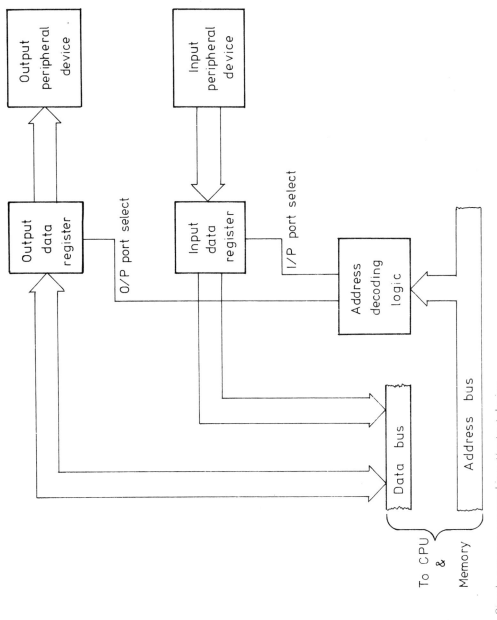

Fig. 9.1 Simple memory mapped input/output device

Mnemonic	Comments
LDA address address	Load accumulator with data held in the input port data register selected by the 16-bit address.
STA address address	Store contents of accumulator in selected RAM memory location.

Some processors have unique opcodes that are only used for input/output data transfer. In this case, the CPU when executing an input/output instruction will select the interface device by a special control line and transfer data along the data bus in the normal way to the selected port register.

9.1   Control of input/output data transfer operations

A microprocessor system may very often be required to perform a number of different tasks. Typical examples are: receiving data from an input peripheral; processing data in a specific way; or feeding results to a second peripheral. The microprocessor may also be required to carry out, apparently simultaneously, other distinct but non-related tasks.

Control of these multiple operations, particularly the transfer of data to and from external peripheral devices may be carried out in three ways:

1) program controlled unconditional data transfer;
2) program controlled conditional data transfer;
3) interrupt control.

9.2   Program controlled unconditional data transfer

This method is the simplest way in which the initiation of any data transfer operation to and from a peripheral can be controlled. It consists of placing instructions in the program sequence that will implement an input/output data transfer operation when that part of the program is reached. The general principle is explained in Fig. 9.2 using both special input/output instructions (input or output), and opcodes that control the transfer of data to memory mapped input/output interface devices.

The major disadvantage with unconditional input/output data transfer is that it can only be used in situations where it is known that either an output device is ready to accept data or an input device has valid data ready to be read into the CPU accumulator. Unfortunately, in a practical situation this is not always the case. For example, a printer may be already printing one character when the program implements an instruction that requires a further character to be printed. Although the program can go through the sequence of transferring the character to the output device, the printer will not be able to print this next character (unless it was specially stored in a buffer register) and the data would therefore be lost.

In a similar way, the monitoring of a keyboard to ensure that no key operations were missed would have to be carried out almost continuously if unconditional input data transfer was used. Even then a problem still occurs when the same key information is recorded as on the last occasion the keyboard was examined. The difficulty now is in distinguishing between valid data in the form of a repeat operation when the same key has been pressed again, or invalid data because the key button is still being held down

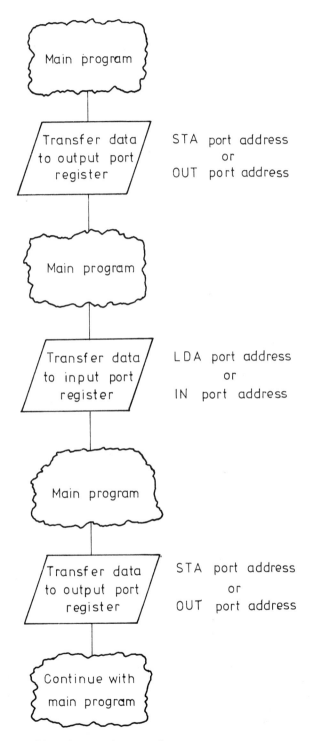

Fig. 9.2   Unconditional input/output data transfer program sequence

from a previous action which has already been recorded. In both of these situations the program could read the keyboard input interface device but in only one case would the data be valid.

Program controlled unconditional input/output data transfer although simple to implement cannot be used unless it can be assured that each time the input/output software instruction is being executed it will result in a valid transfer of information between the microprocessor system and the peripheral device.

9.3　Program controlled conditional data transfer

In this method of input/output data transfer the CPU of the microprocessor system must firstly determine whether the right conditions exist before the actual data transfer operations take place under program control — hence data transfer is conditional on a predetermined set of circumstances.

If, for example, one of the tasks of a microcomputer is to accept data from a teletypewriter keyboard, then a program could be written to examine periodically the input port to which the teletypewriter is connected. When data is ready, the program will include instructions that will transfer the data into the CPU; otherwise the microprocessor will revert to one of its other tasks. A common method used to indicate the presence of data at a peripheral device is to set a status flag referred to as the **data ready flag**. If the flag remains reset the microprocessor will know that no information is available for transfer.

The only major question left unanswered is how often the teletypewriter peripheral must be examined. Should the computer program be arranged so that a long time is spent checking the input peripheral, so wasting processing time; or should it spend most of its time processing, so increasing the possibility of missing input data? In the case of a teletypewriter the maximum speed of typing is 10 characters per second. Therefore, to ensure that no characters are missed, the input peripheral would have to be examined at best every 100 ms to see whether the data ready flag is set.

A possible outline program using these techniques is shown in Fig. 9.3.

Although this type of program is feasible, a number of problems may occur. Firstly, it is extremely difficult to say how many instructions in the main program will take up slightly less than 100 ms, particularly when conditional branch statements are included. Secondly, although the maximum speed of typing is 10 characters per second, there will be long periods of time when no information at all is being entered via the keyboard.

The repeated testing of the input peripheral status flag takes up processing time, and the test instructions require considerable store space. For these reasons program-controlled input/output is not often used where the microprocessor is required to perform several tasks whose needs for servicing are asynchronous or random.

One of the additional facilities required when any form of conditional input/output transfer is to be used is the presence of a status flag. Although this flag could be situated in the peripheral device it is normally found in the input/output interface unit. The flag will need to indicate automatically whether a transfer operation can take place, and must be capable of having its status read into the CPU. Once flag information is in the accumulator of the CPU, any decision on actually implementing a data transfer operation can be made using standard conditional jump or branch instructions.

The hardware circuitry necessary for a conditional data transfer operation is shown in Fig. 9.4. The input data register has a tri-state output facility which will be enabled from the address decoder logic circuit. This will occur when the correct 16-bit binary pattern appears on the address bus and changes the logic level output of line 3 from the decoder. A second device which also has a tristate output facility is the RS flip-flop, acting as a status flag. In the case of this circuit, when a specific address is used, line 3 of the decoder

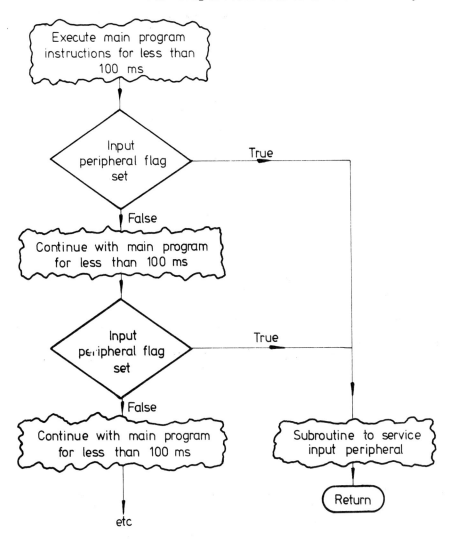

Fig. 9.3 Conditional input data transfer control of TTY keyboard

logic will change state enabling the output facility of the flip-flop and connecting the Q output to one of the data bus lines. In the example of Fig. 9.4 the Q output is connected to the D0 line. In practice this does not have to be the case and any of the data bus lines could be used. Once the flag output has been enabled the data bus can be read into the accumulator of the CPU and the D0 bit of 8-bit word tested to determine the flag status.

Setting the flag is initiated by the peripheral device; thus indicating when a data transfer operation is to take place. After the transfer of data into the CPU, as a result of a 'data ready' flag indication, the status flag must be reset. If this was not done a false indication would exist that a further transfer operation is required. In some interfaces the flag is automatically reset following a flag output read operation. For the diagram of Fig. 9.4 a specific reset operation is required and is achieved by asserting line 1 of the address decoder logic.

The general outline of the software program to be used in conjunction with the

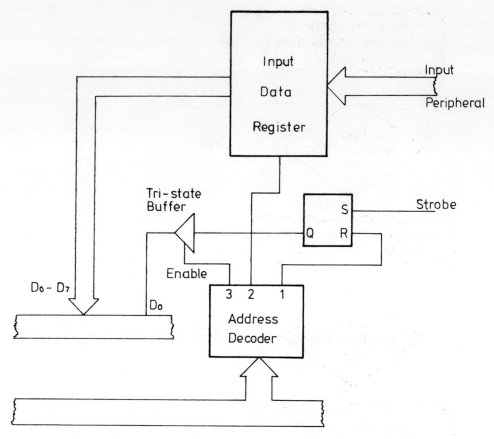

Fig. 9.4   Conditional data transfer hardware

hardware interface is shown in Fig. 9.5. It should be appreciated that the state of the interface flag can only be determined after it has been read into the accumulator of the CPU. Various instructions can be used for this task, the most effective being shift instructions that place the appropriate bit in the carry flag of the CPU status register (condition code register).

Returning to the example of gathering information from the teletypewriter keyboard under conditional data control as illustrated in Fig. 9.3, a number of problems may occur. Firstly, it is extremely difficult to say how many instructions in the main program will take up slightly less then 100 ms. This is particularly true when conditional jump or branch instructions are included. Secondly, although the maximum speed of typing is 10 characters per second, there will be long periods of time when no information at all is being entered via the keyboard. The repeated testing of the input peripheral status flag takes up processing time and the test instructions require considerable store space. For these reasons, program controlled conditional data transfer is not often used where the microprocessor is required to service peripheral devices whose needs are asynchronous.

9.4   Interrupt control

An alternative to program controlled input/output data transfer is to allow the

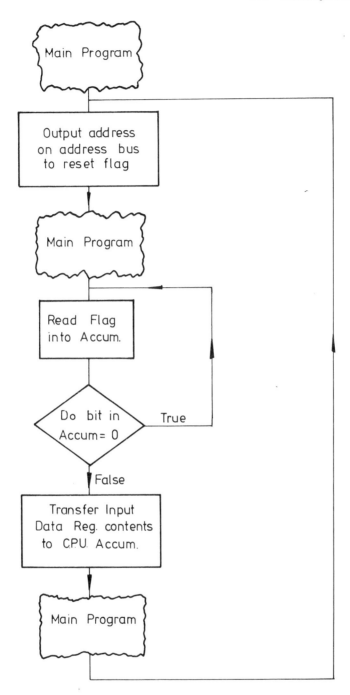

Fig. 9.5   Flowchart for conditional data transfer

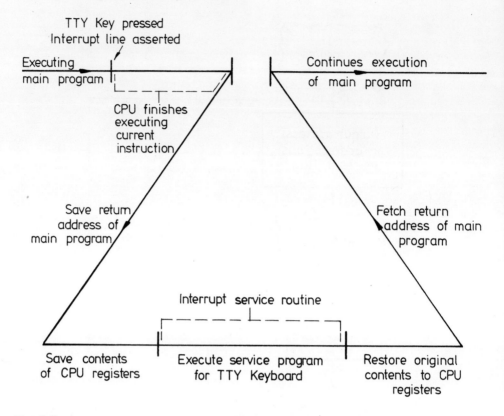

Fig. 9.6   Interrupt sequence

microprocessor to continue executing a program until a peripheral device signals that it requires attention. At this point the CPU breaks off from the execution of the main program and executes a different program stored in memory that will deal with the peripheral device. After servicing the peripheral device the CPU will return to the original program at the point where it was interrupted.

In most systems the ability to interrupt the main program is achieved by changing the logic level on a special control line of the microprocessor I.C. called the **interrupt** line. When this line is asserted by the peripheral device that requires attention, the following events take place:

1) execution of the main program ceases;
2) contents of the program counter and possibly other working registers are stored away on the stack part of the memory;
3) program jumps to a specified memory location.

If the example of the teletypewriter is used, when one of the keys is operated an interrupt signal is produced which informs the CPU that the device requires servicing. It is then, and only then, that the microprocessor will break off from executing the main program. The interrupt sequence for a teletypewriter keyboard is shown in Fig. 9.6.

9.4.1   Interrupt instructions and control
Microprocessors normally have the facility to enable the interrupt line and so allow the CPU to respond to an interrupt signal; or to disable the interrupt line, thus causing the CPU to ignore any interrupt request. This latter requirement may be necessary if the

main program is entering a section such as a software timing loop which should not be interrupted. Interrupt control is normally achieved by using a single flip-flop in the CPU as an interrupt status flag and including instructions that the programmer can use to set or reset the flag. If the interrupt facility has previously been enabled (say status flag reset), and an interrupt occurs, the flag is set. This has the effect of disabling the interrupt line and preventing the CPU from responding to any other interrupt requests until the current interrupt service routine has been completed. After final execution of all the program instructions in the interrupt service routine, the interrupt flag is changed by a special flag reset instruction. This action allows the CPU to respond to the next interrupt request when it occurs.

Software control of the status flag is typically done with instructions such as disable interrupt (DI) and enable interrupt (EI), which can be inserted anywhere in a program. The last instruction in the interrupt service routine is normally a return from interrupt (RTI) instruction. This is a special instruction that will cause the CPU to return to the main program at the point where it left off when it was interrupted. In some microprocessors, the RTI instruction also automatically causes the contents of certain CPU registers that were saved from the main program to be returned from the stack.

9.4.2 Interrupt example

A simple use of the interrupt facility may be explained by considering the connection of a keyboard to the CPU. The keyboard will produce, via an onboard encoder, the ASCII code for any key pressed. This data will be stored in an input port register. A strobe signal is also generated whenever a code key is pressed, and this will be used as the interrupt signal.

The keyboard interrupt service routine consists of a program that will read the ASCII code stored in the data register of the input port, and store the character in a selected memory location. In the CPU system considered here, the interrupt facility is enabled by resetting the interrupt status flag, and the interrupt line ($\overline{\text{INT}}$) is asserted by being taken to a low logic level. The hardware arrangement for the system is shown in Fig. 9.7 and the software layout in Fig. 9.8.

Considering Fig. 9.8 memory location 0000 (hex) to 01FF (hex) contains the main program, and the keyboard interrupt service routine (KISR) is stored in location 035F (hex) to 036D (hex). The first instruction in the main program is to enable the interrupt facility, which will reset the interrupt flag of Fig. 9.7. If a key is pressed while the CPU is executing the instruction at 0055 the ASCII code will be entered into the data register. At the same time a strobe pulse is produced and the $\overline{\text{INT}}$ line asserted. After executing the instruction at 0055, the CPU will check the status of the interrupt flag. If this is in the reset condition an interrupt sequence will be initiated, and the status flag is automatically set to disable the interrupt facility.

The contents of the program counter, at present indicating the next instruction in the main program to be executed, are stored in the area of memory allocated to the stack. The program counter is now loaded with 035F, which is the starting address of the keyboard interrupt service routine. The service routine will now arrange for the data register in the input port to be read, and its contents stored in a selected memory location. Following the last line of the KISR, the interrupt enable instruction causes the CPU status flag to be reset. Execution of the return from interrupt instruction results in the stack being pulled and its contents, 0056 (hex), being loaded into the program counter. This results in a return to the main program at the point it reached when it was initially interrupted.

In the simple example considered the strobe pulse from the keyboard must be short otherwise the $\overline{\text{INT}}$ line will still be low when a return to the main program occurs. On its own this is of no consequence, but as the status flag is now reset, a repeat interrupt

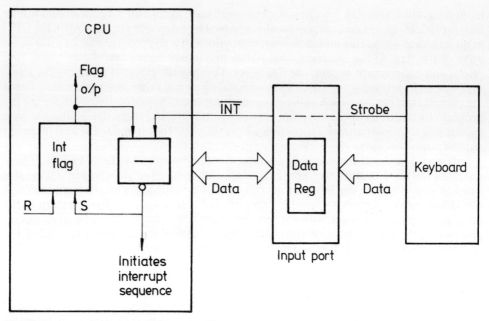

Fig. 9.7   Keyboard connection with interrupt

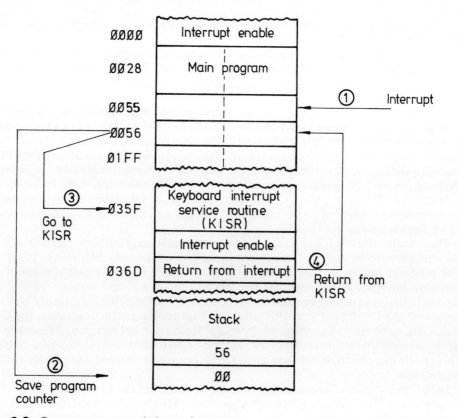

Fig. 9.8   Program sequence during an interrupt

sequence will be initiated for the same character. Normally this type of action can be prevented by placing an interrupt flag in the input port as well as in the CPU.

9.4.3 Interrupt service routine address

One main question still remains unanswered, and that is how the CPU knows where the interrupt service routine is situated. The answer to this will vary from one microprocessor to the next. In some systems the occurrence of an interrupt causes the CPU to jump to a specified memory location. Here the interrupt service routine itself may be stored or, as is more usual, the programmer has placed a form of branch instruction that causes a jump to another part of the memory. This is referred to as an **interrupt vector** and will normally consist of two bytes that, when loaded into the program counter, form the address of where the CPU will go for the first instruction of the interrupt service routine.

   An alternative method of branching is for the peripheral device itself or its associated interface hardware to supply the CPU with the address where the interrupt service routine is located in memory. This method has the disadvantage of requiring additional hardware, external to the CPU or peripheral device.

9.4.4 Multiple interrupts

In a microprocessor system it is usual for only one standard interrupt request line to be provided. When a number of peripheral devices require interrupt facilities they are connected to the single interrupt line in a wired-OR configuration (see p. 34). The problem then arises, if an interrupt is initiated, to distinguish which device is calling for attention. There are a number of solutions to this problem. Some require extra hardware in the form of an interrupt arbitrator circuit, while a software solution is to use a **polling** technique on the peripheral devices.

   Polling means that the CPU interrogates each of the input/output ports by reading the state of an interrupt request flag until it finds a flag which is set. Once the interrupting device is found, the contents of the CPU registers are saved and the peripheral device is then serviced. The contents of the CPU registers will be pushed onto the stack, to be retrieved at the end of the peripheral service operation. Depending on which device is found to be wanting attention the address of an appropriate service subroutine is loaded into the program counter. After the subroutine is executed the original states of the CPU registers are pulled from the stack and the program continues from where it left off.

   A general flow diagram to deal with multiple.interrupts is shown in Fig. 9.9.

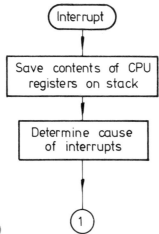

Fig. 9.9 (continued overleaf)

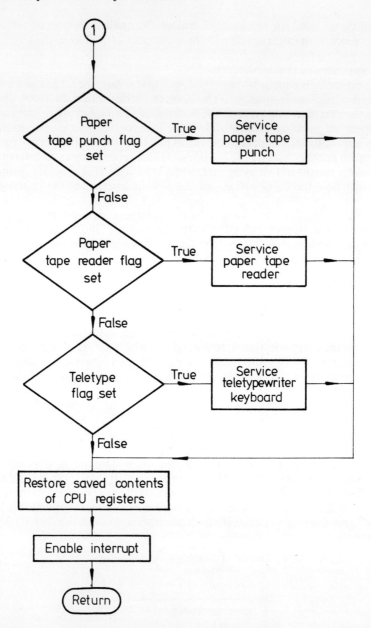

Fig. 9.9   Software polling of peripheral devices

The polling chain provides a method of establishing the cause of an interrupt, and also establishes a priority ranking of the devices attached to the interrupt line. it is quite possible for a situation to exist where more than one device is simultaneously asserting the interrupt line. By using the **skip chain** principle the device highest up in the polling chain will be serviced first.

When establishing a priority sequence for peripheral devices it is normal practice to give the faster acting devices the higher priorities.

The alternative to software polling is to use a hardware arbitrator circuit where the CPU responds to an interrupt request by sending out on a separate line an interrupt acknowledge signal (INTA) to each device. Only the device that generated the original interrupt request signal will respond; it does this by supplying the CPU with the starting address of its interrupt service routine. To cater for simultaneous interrupt from two or more devices the CPU carries out a hardware form of polling called **daisy chaining**. In this process the CPU first sends the interrupt acknowledge signal to the highest priority device. If this is not the interrupting device the interrupt acknowledge signal is passed down the line to the next highest priority device, and so on until the interrupting device is found. This device then sends to the CPU the address of its interrupt service routine. Because of the extra logic involved in this arrangement, microprocessor manufacturers that use this technique also produce special programmable interrupt control integrated circuits.

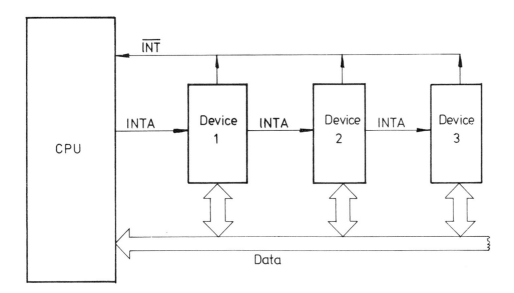

Fig. 9.10   Daisy chaining of peripheral devices

9.4.5   Interrupting an interrupt service routine

In the normal course of events, if the microprocessor has been interrupted, and is already executing an interrupt service routine, the interrupt status flag in the CPU will have been set and any further interrupt facility disabled. However, if one of the first instructions in the interrupt service routine is an EI (enable interrupt) instruction then the CPU interrupt flag will be reset. The consequence of this would be that a later interrupt request from another device would cause the existing interrupt service routine to be interrupted. The contents of the program counter and the CPU registers would be stored on the stack and a jump made to the starting address of the new interrupt service routine. On completion of this routine, the RTI (return from interrupt) instruction causes the CPU to return to the first interrupt service routine and complete its execution.

9.5　Interrupts in the 6802

The 6802 CPU chip has three interrupt request lines. These are:

1) $\overline{\text{IRQ}}$ — interrupt request;
2) $\overline{\text{Reset}}$ — reset;
3) $\overline{\text{NMI}}$ — non-maskable interrupt.

The $\overline{\text{IRQ}}$ line is the standard interrupt request facility and is connected to most of the peripheral devices requiring interrupt facilities. Each peripheral interface device needs the ability to enable the CPU interrupt line, and for this reason all the peripheral interrupt request lines are connected in a wired-OR configuration. The Reset line is used to initialise and start the MPU from a powerdown condition by causing a jump to the start of the ROM program for a microprocessor-based system, or to the ROM monitor if the system is configured as a microcomputer (see p. 180). $\overline{\text{NMI}}$ is a line that when asserted will always cause an interrupt to take place irrespective of the CPU interrupt status flag condition. For this reason NMI is reserved for catastrophic situations such as power supply failures. In this event, the NMI routine is able to save the states of the CPU registers and thus, provided that the memory has a standby emergency supply, the main program execution will recommence after supplies are restored. The time taken to save the registers is negligible compared to the time taken for the power supply capacitance to discharge to the point that the supply is deemed to have failed.

All three interrupt facilities use the interrupt vector technique to locate the individual service routines. In standard 6802 systems the highest locations in the memory contain the addresses of routines which when executed service the interrupt. Thus the vectored system automatically points the CPU to the appropriate routine.

9.5.1　$\overline{\text{IRQ}}$

On receiving an $\overline{\text{IRQ}}$ signal, the processor will wait until the current instruction being executed is completed before recognising the request. Provided that the interrupt mask bit in the condition code register (bit 4 — I) is not set the CPU will begin an interrupt sequence. The index register, program counter, accumulators and condition codes register are all automatically stored away on the stack. Next the CPU will respond to the interrupt request by setting the interrupt mask bit (I) in the condition codes register. The purpose of this is to ensure that once an interrupt is acknowledged it will not itself be interrupted until the current interrupt routine is finished. After setting the I bit high the processor jumps to memory locations FFF8 and FFF9 (hex). Stored at these two memory locations is the 16-bit address of the IRQ interrupt service routine. The CPU now branches to this address and commences execution of either a straight interrupt service routine or a software poll if more than one device is connected to the $\overline{\text{IRQ}}$ line.

9.5.2　Reset

When this line is asserted, the CPU will start execution of a routine to initialise the processor from its reset condition. This will consist of the CPU going to memory locations FFFE and FFFF (hex) and loading the program counter with the contents of these locations. The address stored in FFFE and FFFF (hex) is the starting address of the reset service routine. During the restart operation the interrupt mask bit in the condition codes register is set and must be reset before the CPU can be interrupted by $\overline{\text{IRQ}}$.

9.5.3　$\overline{\text{NMI}}$

A low-going edge on this input requests that a non-maskable interrupt sequence be generated. As in the case of the $\overline{\text{IRQ}}$ signal, the processor will complete the current instruction that is being executed before it recognises the $\overline{\text{NMI}}$ signal. The interrupt mask bit in the condition codes register has no effect on the $\overline{\text{NMI}}$ request. The index register, program counter, accumulators and condition codes register are stored away on the stack. The CPU now goes to FFFC and FFFD (hex) in which is stored the vector address of the $\overline{\text{NMI}}$ interrupt service routine. This address is loaded into the program counter causing a branch to the start of the non-maskable interrupt routine in memory.

9.5.4 SWI instruction

Besides the three hardware interrupt facilities, a single-byte software interrupt instruction (SWI) is also provided in the instruction set. If the CPU executes a SWI instruction in a program it will carry out a similar action to that implemented when an $\overline{\text{IRQ}}$ signal is received, i.e. the program counter, index register, accumulators and condition codes register are stored on the stack and a vector address is picked up from memory locations FFFA and FFFB.

In some microcomputers the software interrupt instruction is used as a debugging aid for program development. When a SWI instruction is executed, the vector address loaded into the program counter will cause a jump to a subroutine within the systems monitor. The subroutine called will cause a print on the output display of all the main register contents. This is an invaluable method of tracing through the actual execution of a program, particularly when it is not functioning as intended.

A summary of the vector address locations for all the interrupt facilities in the 6802 is shown in Table 9.1.

Table 9.1   6802 interrupt vector address locations

Memory location	Vector address assignment
FFF8	IRQ most significant byte
FFF9	IRQ least significant byte
FFFA	SWI most significant byte
FFFB	SWI least significant byte
FFFC	NMI most significant byte
FFFD	NMI least significant byte
FFFE	Reset most significant byte
FFFF	Reset least significant byte

9.5.5 IRQ interrupt example

The conditions existing in memory and in the CPU registers during the execution of the main program and before an interrupt occurs are shown in Fig. 9.11. Placing the CLI instruction early, but not necessarily first, in the main program will clear the interrupt bit in the condition codes register. Memory locations FFF8 and FFF9 already hold the vector address of the interrupt service routine, and the stack pointer has been loaded with Ø3FF.

If an IRQ interrupt occurs when the CPU is executing the instruction at 013B (hex), the sequence of events on completion of the instruction would be as follows.

1)   Program counter low-order 8 bits (3C hex) transferred to memory location Ø3FF.
2)   Program counter high-order 8 bits (Ø1 hex) transferred to memory location Ø3FE.
3)   Index register contents transferred to Ø3FD and Ø3FC.
4)   Contents of accumulator A and B transferred to Ø3FB and Ø3FA.
5)   Condition codes register contents transferred to Ø3F9.
6)   Program counter contents loaded with Ø2ØØ from FFF8 and FFF9.

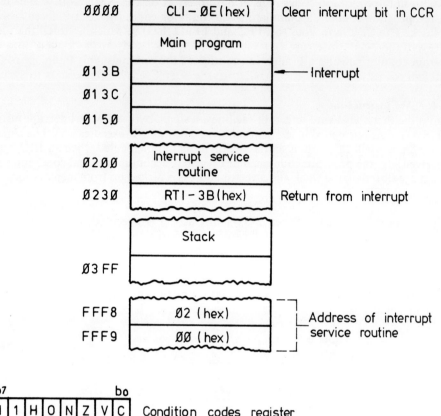

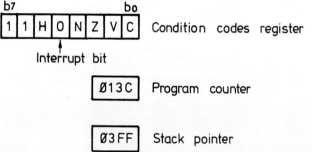

Fig. 9.11   Memory and register conditions before an interrupt

7)   Interrupt flag bit in condition codes register set to 1.
8)   Commence execution of interrupt service routine.

At the end of the interrupt service routine the interrupt bit does not need to be cleared, because on executing the RTI instruction the stack is pulled and the old status of the condition codes register is returned. As the I bit in this register was set to 0, the interrupt facility is automatically re-enabled.

9.6   Interrupts in the 6502

The hardware interrupt facilities in the 6502 are identical to those of the 6802 except that the interrupt vector addresses are stored in different memory locations. Software interrupt is obtained by a break (BRK) instruction which sets the interrupt (I) bit in the status register and also a break (B) bit which is specific to the 6502. However, the vector address for the instruction is the same as that for an IRQ. Establishing whether a BRK or IRQ interrupt service routine is to be initiated can be achieved by first polling the I and B bits of the status register.

Details of the memory locations holding the interrupt vector addresses are shown in Table 9.2.

Table 9.2 6502 interrupt vector address locations

Memory location	Vector address assignment
FFFA	NMI least significant byte
FFFB	NMI most significant byte
FFFC	Reset least significant byte
FFFD	Reset most significant byte
FFFE	IRQ and BRK least significant byte
FFFF	IRQ and BRK most significant byte

9.7 Interrupts in the 8085

The 8085 has five interrupt request lines. These are:

1) INTR — interrupt request;
2) RST 5.5 — restart 5.5;
3) RST 6.5 — restart 6.5;
4) RST 7.5 — restart 7.5;
5) TRAP — trap (restart).

The INTR is the general purpose interrupt request line of the 8085 and behaves in a similar fashion to the INT line of the 8080. This is a maskable line which means that it is only operable if a mask bit (flip-flop flag) in the CPU is in the correct state. There are also three further maskable interrupts, RST 5.5, RST 6.5, and RST 7.5, of which the 7.5 line has the highest priority and 5.5 the lowest priority. The 8085 has a non maskable interrupt TRAP which has the highest priority of all the interrupt lines and is useful for catastrophic events such as power failure.

When a number of peripheral devices are generating interrupt signals onto one of the interrupt lines, and a priority system is required, then external logic must be used to determine the priority of the individual interrupts.

9.7.1 INTR
When this line is taken high the 8085 CPU action will be interrupted provided that the interrupt facility has been enabled earlier in the program. On receiving an interrupt request the CPU finishes executing the current instruction and then acknowledges the interrupt by sending out an INTA (interrupt acknowledge) signal. The interrupting device, on receiving the INTA signal, places an instruction onto the data bus. Typically, this instruction is one of the special single-byte RST subroutine call instructions. The CPU then carries out a fetch-execute cycle on the instruction, which in turn causes a branch to the appropriate address associated with that specific RST instruction. It is at this address that further instructions associated with the service routine for the interrupting device are stored.

As described in Section 8.6.4, any one of eight RST instructions can be generated by

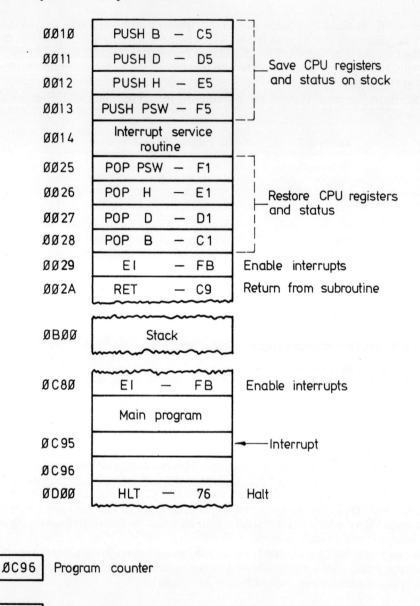

0010	PUSH B — C5	
0011	PUSH D — D5	Save CPU registers and status on stock
0012	PUSH H — E5	
0013	PUSH PSW — F5	
0014	Interrupt service routine	
0025	POP PSW — F1	
0026	POP H — E1	Restore CPU registers and status
0027	POP D — D1	
0028	POP B — C1	
0029	EI — FB	Enable interrupts
002A	RET — C9	Return from subroutine
0B00	Stack	
0C80	EI — FB	Enable interrupts
	Main program	
0C95		◄——Interrupt
0C96		
0D00	HLT — 76	Halt

0C96	Program counter

0B00	Stack pointer

Fig. 9.12 Memory and register conditions before an interrupt

the peripheral device. This in turn will cause program control to be transferred to one of eight memory locations after storing the current contents of the program counter on the stack. Details of the RST instructions are shown in Table 8.2 on page 97.

The appropriate interrupt service routine may be written in the bytes provided between each RST starting address; or, as is more common, a jump instruction included that will cause transfer to another area of memory. The latter method of handling interrupts has the advantage that eight different devices can interrupt the microprocessor and each device can immediately direct the CPU to a different interrupt subroutine.

If the INTR interrupt facility is required, the programmer must ensure that the EI (enable interrupt) instruction is written somewhere into the program prior to the CPU being interrupted. Once an interrupt occurs, all further interrupts are disabled until the EI instruction is executed again. The programmer can similarly disable all further interrupts from affecting the CPU by using the DI (diable interrupt) instruction.

9.7.2 RST 5.5

The RST 5.5 interrupt action is asserted by a high level on its input. When a logic 1 level is applied to the RST 5.5 line the CPU automatically places on the stack the current contents of the program counter and vectors to memory address ØØ2C (hex). It is assumed that at this memory location there will be an instruction which causes a jump to an area of memory where the service routine for the device causing the interrupt is stored.

RST 5.5 is a maskable interrupt facility. Only if the mask bit is in the correct state will a high level on the RST 5.5 line cause an interrupt sequence to occur. The setting of the mask bit is controlled by the software instruction SIM (set interrupt mask). The servicing of an interrupt disables all future interrupts until an EI (enable interrupt) is executed.

9.7.3 RST 6.5

The action of the RST 6.5 interrupt line is identical to that of RST 5.5 except that the CPU, after an interrupt signal, vectors to memory location ØØ34 (hex) not ØØ2C (hex) as for RST 5.5.

9.7.4 RST 7.5

For the RST 7.5 line to generate an interrupt action, a rising edge signal is required (positive going pulse). The RST 7.5 request flip-flop in the 8085 CPU remains set until the request is serviced, then it is reset automatically and disables any further interrupts on the RST 7.5 line. This flip-flop may also be reset by the SIM instruction.

On responding to an interrupt signal on the RST 7.5 line, the CPU pushes the program counter contents on the stack and vectors to memory location ØØ3C (hex).

9.7.5 TRAP

The TRAP input is recognised in the same way as any other input except that it is not affected by any flag or mask. The interrupt input will also respond to either edge or level sensitive signals. When a high level signal or positive edge is applied to the TRAP input the CPU will always push the contents of the program counter onto the stack and vector to memory location ØØ24 (hex).

The TRAP input has the highest priority should requests occur at the same time on other interrupt lines.

A summary of the memory location addresses applicable for interrupt operations are shown in Table 9.3.

Table 9.3 8085 interrupt address locations

Memory address branched to	Interrupt type
ØØ24	TRAP
ØØ2C	RST 5.5
ØØ34	RST 6.5
ØØ3C	RST 7.5
*	INTR

*The address branched to depends on the instruction provided to the CPU when the interrupt signal is acknowledged.

9.7.6 INTR interrupt example

Basing the example on the memory map of Fig. 9.12 it can be seen that the main program is stored in memory locations ØC8Ø to ØDØØ with an EI (enable interrupt) instruction early on in the program. Starting at ØØ1Ø is the interrupt service routine which means that an RST2 instruction must be placed on the data bus by the interrupting peripheral device. Because instructions RST3 to RST6 will never be used in this program more memory locations than the normal eight bytes can be utilised as part of the interrupt service routine. The high end of the stack is at ØBØØ, with the stack pointer register being decremented as data is stored.

If the CPU is interrupted while an instruction at, say, ØC95 is being implemented, at the end of the execute cycle the following operations will take place.

1)   INTA signal sent to peripheral device.
2)   All further interrupts disabled.
3)   RST2 instruction sent to CPU from peripheral device.
4)   Most significant byte of program counter (ØC hex) stored at ØAFF (hex).
5)   Least significant byte of program counter (96 hex) stored at ØAFE (hex).
6)   Program counter loaded with ØØ1Ø.
7)   CPU registers and status condition stored on stack.
8)   Main part of interrupt service routine executed.

In many cases it is not necessary to store all, or even any, of the CPU registers and status on the stack. The number of PUSH instructions used will depend on the nature of the interrupt service routine. Unlike the 6800 no automatic storing of register contents takes place.

At the end of the interrupt service routine the contents of the CPU registers held during the main part of the program must be restored from where they are held on the stack. The interrupt facility is then enabled and the RET instruction causes the program counter to be loaded from the stack with ØC96, which is the return address of the next instruction to be executed in the main program.

9.8   Interrupts in the Z80

The Z80 CPU has two interrupt input lines: $\overline{\text{NMI}}$ and $\overline{\text{INT}}$. The non-maskable $\overline{\text{NMI}}$ line can not be disabled by the programmer, whereas the maskable $\overline{\text{INT}}$ line can be selectively enabled or disabled by the instructions EI (enable interrupt) and DI (disable interrupt) respectively. These instructions control an interrupt enable flip-flop (IFF) in the CPU. When the IFF is reset an interrupt request will not be accepted by the CPU.

9.8.1 $\overline{\text{NMI}}$

When the $\overline{\text{NMI}}$ line is taken low, the CPU will recognise the interrupt request at the end of executing the current instruction and irrespective of the status of the interrupt enable flip-flop. The present contents of the program counter are stored on the stack and the program counter is then automatically loaded with ØØ66 (hex).

9.8.2 $\overline{\text{INT}}$

The CPU can be programmed, by using the IM (interrupt mode) instruction, to respond to a $\overline{\text{INT}}$ signal in any one of three possible ways, or **modes**.

Mode 0   Selected by the instruction IM0 this is exactly the same as the method used by the 8085. The interrupting device can place any instruction (single-, two- or three-byte) on the data bus and the CPU will execute it.

Mode 1   When this mode is selected by the programmer using the instruction IM1 the

CPU will respond to an interrupt by automatically branching to memory location Ø Ø 38 (hex), having previously stored the return address of the main program on the stack.

Mode 2 This mode uses the interrupt vector (I) register to help determine where in memory the address of the interrupt service routine is stored. By this method a single byte from the peripheral can cause an indirect call to be made to any memory location. The instruction that selects this mode of interrupt is IM2.

9.8.3 Z80 mode 2 interrupt example

The software instructions necessary to implement a mode 2 $\overline{\text{INT}}$ interrupt are shown in

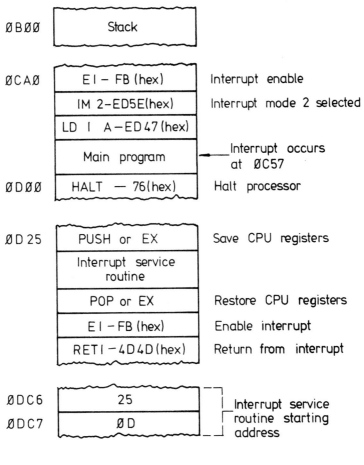

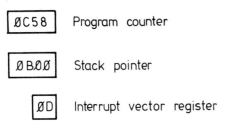

Fig. 9.13 Memory and register conditions before an interrupt

Fig. 9.13. The main program situated between memory locations ØCAØ and ØDØØ contains both EI and IM2 instructions. In the Z80, saving the contents of CPU registers and status can be achieved by using an exchange register instruction or the standard push instruction available on the 8080. The amount of CPU information stored from the main program during an interrupt will depend on the type of instructions used in the interrupt service routine. It should be noted from Fig. 9.13 that prior to an interrupt occurring the interrupt vector register must have been loaded from the main program with the byte ØD. This byte represents the most significant byte of the memory location address where the low-order starting address byte for the interrupt service routine is stored.

If an interrupt occurs while the main program is dealing with an instruction at ØC57 the interrupt request will be acknowledged at the end of the execute cycle and the following sequence initiated.

1) Interrupt enable flip-flop (IFF) reset and all further interrupts disabled.
2) Peripheral device places C6 (hex) onto data bus.
3) Contents of program counter, ØC58 (hex), pushed onto stack.
4) Contents of interrupt vector register, ØD (hex), and data from peripheral device, C6 (hex), used as pointer to memory location ØDC6.
5) Contents of ØDC6 and ØDC7, ØD25 (hex), loaded into program counter.
6) CPU jumps to start of interrupt service routine at ØD25 (hex).
7) CPU register contents saved as appropriate.
8) Main part of interrupt service routine executed.

At the end of the interrupt service routine the IFF flag is set by the EI instruction. The RETI (return from interrupt) instruction causes the stack to be pulled, and the address of the next instruction which will be executed in the main program to be loaded into the program counter. A return is then made to the main program.

10
LSI input/output devices

Chapter 9 examined the ways in which a microprocessor system could communicate with a peripheral device by using the I/O data transfer methods of: unconditional, conditional or interrupt control. Although hardware circuitry was involved in these operations, the main concept was of input or output data transfer using software instructions. However, in addition to selecting the most appropriate method of transferring data, other factors also have to be considered. Two of the more important factors are deciding whether the signal that communicates with the peripheral device is to be of a parallel or serial nature, and also the way in which the interface hardware is to be implemented.

10.1 Parallel and serial data transmissions

Although a microprocessor system moves information in parallel form between its major units, the means of transferring data to the peripheral device can either be in serial or parallel form. A parallel signal will consist typically, of an 8-bit binary pattern transmitted along eight parallel signal lines that are connected between the I/O interface unit and the peripheral device. In contrast, the nature of serial transmission is that one bit at a time of the signal is transmitted along a single line. Parallel transfer has the advantage of speed (8 bits at a time), while serial transfer benefits in terms of cost because of the need to have only two signal lines (transmit and receive) plus a common line. Modern digital printers are very often organised to receive parallel data because of the need to achieve a fast printing speed, whereas a VDU may be situated some distance away from the main computer system and will therefore accept and transmit data in serial form.

In the case of both parallel and serial transmission there may be a need for additional lines, often called **handshaking** lines, to control when the flow of data between microprocessor system and peripheral device should take place. The actual number of these handshaking or data management lines will vary according to the application and type of peripheral device. Some peripherals, particularly those working under unconditional data transfer, will require no handshaking signals, whereas many devices will require at least one input or one output line.

These basic principles of signal format are illustrated in Fig. 10.1 and Fig. 10.2 where two handshaking lines called data available (DAV) and data accepted (DAC) are used. When the I/O interface device has received data from the CPU it will send a data available signal to the peripheral. The output peripheral device on receiving the DAV signal can accept the data and then send a data accepted signal back to the CPU via the interface.

10.2 Types of interface hardware

Some interface units will be purpose-designed using digital ICs from the small scale (SSI) and medium scale (MSI) range of which logic gates and registers are typical examples.

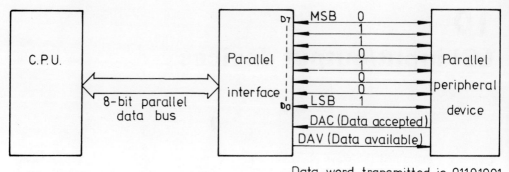

Data word transmitted is 01101001

Fig. 10.1   Parallel data transfer with handshake

This type of interface circuit will possibly be very simple in its purpose but have the advantage of cheapness to implement. A simple example of a purpose-designed dedicated interface circuit is shown in Fig. 10.3. The peripheral device in this example is a set of eight lights which are required under certain conditions to display the 8-bit word that appears on the data bus. The parallel data register and logic gate circuits make up the output interface circuit.

Transfer of data to the register will occur when the correct address appears on the address bus and the R/$\overline{\text{W}}$ (read/write) line is low. This can be produced under software control by using a write instruction to a memory location. When the address decoder output is at logic 1 and the R/$\overline{\text{W}}$ line is at logic 0, the negative edge of the $\emptyset_2$ timing pulse will cause the AND gate output to go low producing a negative edge on the register clock input and a write or store operation into the register. The byte on the data bus is now held in the register and switches on the lights according to the binary pattern stored.

An alternative option to the fixed circuitry dedicated type of interface just described is to use a general purpose large scale integration (LSI) device. This type of single IC can be programmed by software to suit the interfacing requirements of a specific peripheral device. Both parallel and serial interface ICs are available, with each manufacturer using their own slightly different names to identify the type of device. Examples of some of the more common names are given below.

Parallel I/O interface LSI device   Peripheral Interface Adapter (PIA)
                                     Parallel Input/Output (PIO)
                                     Versatile Interface Adapter (VIA)

Serial I/O interface LSI device   Asynchronous Interface Adaptor (ACIA)
                                     Universal Asynchronous Receiver/Transmitter
                                     (UART)

In practical terms there are as many serial and parallel I/O chips as there are manufacturers of microprocessors. Therefore, in the descriptive examples that follow, only a representative sample of devices is covered. For the parallel devices the Motorola PIA and Zilog PIO are dealt with, and on the serial side the Motorola ACIA is considered. The understanding of the use of these devices will go a long way towards an appreciation of other LSI I/O interface chips.

Before examining specific manufacturers examples, it may be useful to consider some of the basic features that are available in a general purpose LSI parallel device. Besides providing parallel input or output on all 8 data lines simultaneously, it is also possible to define separately the function of each line (Fig. 10.4). In addition the function and

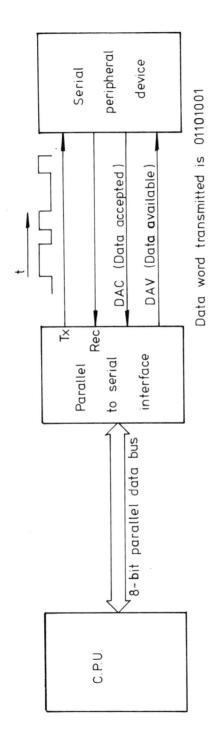

Fig. 10.2   Serial data transfer with handshake

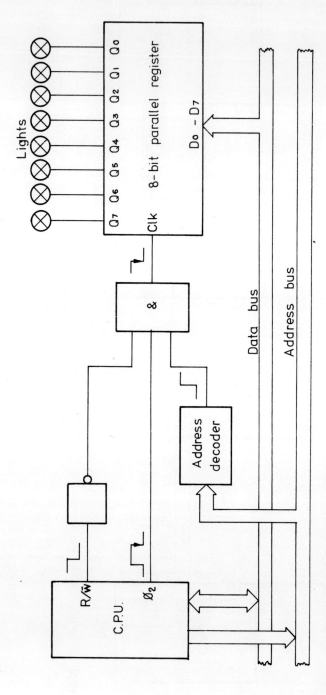

Fig. 10.3 Simple output interface and peripheral device.

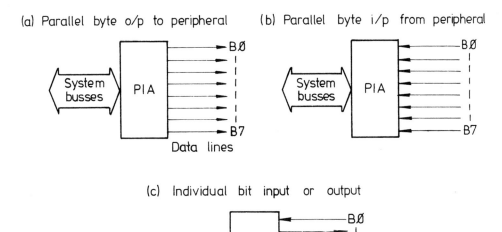

(a) Parallel byte o/p to peripheral   (b) Parallel byte i/p from peripheral

Data lines

(c) Individual bit input or output

Fig. 10.4   Optional configurations for PIA lines

action of handshaking lines must also be established to provide the compatibility of
signal levels between peripheral device and interface. Clearly, because these devices are
capable of so many modes of operation, the exact function required by the user must be
specified. This is usually achieved by writing a control word into a control register within
the device. Each bit of this register is significant in setting up the required operation.
Before any I/O device can be used it must be initialised by being sent instructions on how
it must perform.

The basic block diagram of a parallel LSI interface is shown in Fig. 10.5.

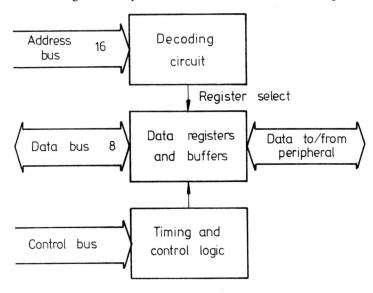

Fig. 10.5   A basic LSI input/output parallel device

10.3   Using the Motorola PIA

10.3.1   A simple control example

Suppose that it was required to monitor an industrial process, and that one of the parameters was measured using an analogue-to-digital converter producing eight output lines. Each of these lines might provide an input to a data line of an 8-bit PIA channel. Further, suppose that the PIA is required to make available this 8-bit word to the CPU so that it may be compared with the desired value. Should the measured value be too large the CPU must output a signal to the control element of the process to reduce the monitored quantity. Conversely, should the output of the analogue-to-digital converter fall below the required value a different signal must advise the process control element to bring about a return of the parameter to the set level.

Suppose that the monitored quantity was temperature; the control element might therefore be the process heater. Assume that the heater is controlled by two lines, each one being decoded by logic gates so that the level on the line has the following significance:

      00   heating off;
      01   heating on.

The PIA has two 8-bit ports or channels denoted A and B; therefore the scheme suggested could be implemented by making the A side an 8-bit input port. The B side would need only two of its lines configured as outputs; see Fig. 10.6.

Both the A and B sides of the PIA comprise three registers. Each register is accessed by the system data bus, and each is treated as a memory location. The valid addresses will depend upon where the PIA is placed within the memory space.

The three registers are the peripheral data register, the data direction register and the control register; see Fig. 10.7.

10.3.2   The register functions

The peripheral data register (PDR)   The data lines from the peripheral are buffered from the system data bus by this data register. Each bit of the data register can be arranged to accept input from either the peripheral or the system. Clearly this means that the lines between the PIA and the peripheral will either be inputs to, or outputs from, the computer system.

When the PIA data register is written to by the processor, the byte on the system data

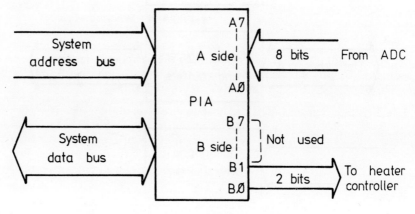

Fig. 10.6   The PIA configured for the suggested industrial process

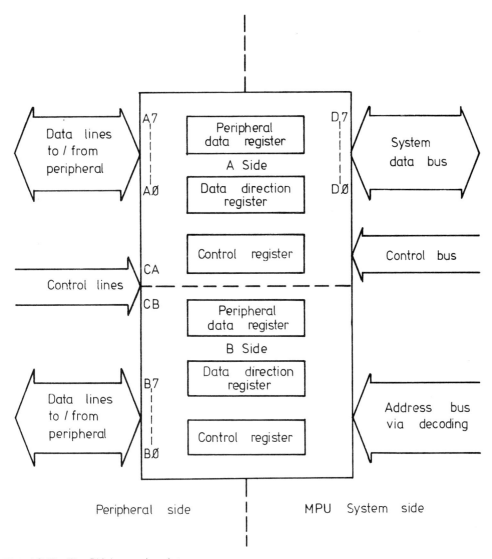

Fig. 10.7 The PIA internal registers

bus will be transferred to the data register. Any lines configured as outputs from the register will automatically transfer the data to the peripheral device.

Reading the PIA data register will take in data from the peripheral to the system data bus and hence to the CPU, for any lines configured as inputs.

The data direction register (DDR)   The data direction register identifies each line of an I/O port as being used only as an input or an output. Addressing the DDR and loading it with 0s configures all of the lines as inputs. Loading with 1s configures the port as a byte output. The DDR can be loaded with a mixed word, so that each bit of the data register will be arranged to transmit or to receive data. The various combinations available on the DDR are illustrated in Fig. 10.8.

The control register   The control register defines the mode in which the port or channel will operate. If a handshaking mode is selected the control lines on the output side of the

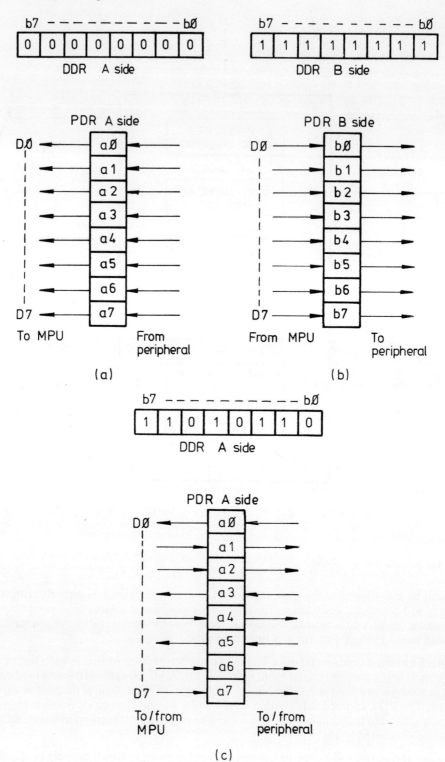

Fig. 10.8 PDR set up as (a) byte input; (b) byte output; (c) bidirectional I/O

PIA will be used to communicate with the peripheral. There are two control lines for each side of the PIA and the way that these are to be used is specified by the state of five of the control register bits. Two bits act as interrupt flags. An interrupt request is acknowledged by the setting of these bits, and they are cleared by the processor reading the data register only during an interrupt service routine.

A most important function is performed by bit 2, since, as will be seen, the data register and the data direction register share an address. In conjunction with the register select lines, bit 2 determines which register will be accessed; in fact bit 2 status arbitrates between them. For operation in a simple input or output mode bit 2 is the only important one in the control register; see Fig. 10.9.

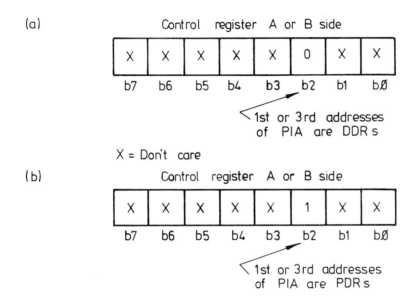

Fig. 10.9   The control register for simple I/O

For the purposes of the example, it may be taken that the addresses relating to the PIA being used are as shown in Table 10.1.

10.3.3   The initialisation routine
It is possible for the reset line of the PIA to be connected to the main system reset line, so that on power up all the registers in the PIA will be cleared. This means that bit 2 of the control register will be clear, or zero, and thus the address 8001 will refer to the data direction register. Similarly, 8003 is the B side DDR address.

If this automatic reset is not arranged it will be necessary to load the accumulator of the CPU with hex code 00 and then store the contents of the accumulator in 8002 and 8004. The normal arrangement, however, is for automatic power up reset to be applied.

The PIA must be told precisely what will be expected of it and the first step is to set up both the A and B sides as either inputs or outputs. In our example scheme it has previously been decided that the A side shall act as a byte input, and this is achieved by loading the accumulator with hex 00 and storing the accumulator contents in 8001, the A side data direction register.

Table 10.1

Hex address	Register	Comments
8001	Peripheral data register	A side (control register bit 2 = 1)
8001	Data direction register	A side (control register bit 2 = 0)
8002	Control register	A side
8003	Peripheral data register	B side (control register bit 2 = 1)
8003	Data direction register	B side (control register bit 2 = 0)
8004	Control register	B side

This done, the B side can be set up with two of its lines, say line 0 and line 1, as outputs by loading the accumulator with hex code 03 and transmitting this to address 8003, the data direction register of the B side. (In this case, the word sent to this register may be any code provided that the two least significant bits are 1. This is because only these two lines will be used.)

The next step is to load each of the control registers with a word that will set bit 2, thus making over the addresses 8001 and 8003 to the peripheral data registers. Once again, the accumulator should be loaded with the appropriate word and the accumulator contents sent to each control register (address 8002 for the A side and 8004 for the B side).

From then on, data from 8001 will be the contents of the A side data buffer (PDR) and data sent to 8003 will be destined for the B side data buffer (PDR).

The initialisation as described would be a longer program than it need be, because of the repeated need to store the accumulator in the extended mode. A more efficient ploy is to make use of the indexed mode of address and load the index register of the CPU with the first address appertaining to the PIA. Each address of the PIA can then be reached by using the appropriate modifier or offset byte.

An example of such a program is listed below.

Address	Hex code	Mnemonic	Comments
0000	CE	LDX	Load the index register with
0001	80	address	the first address in the PIA.
0002	01		
0003	86	LDAA	Load the accumulator with
0004	00	data	00 immediate mode.
0005	A7	STA, X	Store accumulator in DDR
0006	00	data	of the A side of the PIA (8001).
0007	86	LDAA	Load the accumulator with
0008	03	data	03 immediate mode.
0009	A7	STA, X	Store the accumulator in DDR
000A	02	data	of the B side of the PIA (8003).
000B	86	LDAA	Load the accumulator with
000C	07	data	07 immediate mode.
000D	A7	STA, X	Store the control word 07
000E	01	data	in the control registers
000F	A7	STA, X	of both the A and B sides
0010	03	data	(8002 and 8004).

10.4 A control program using the 6800 system

It now only remains to write the program for the system which is to be controlled. The program shown below is intended to follow on from the initialisation routine.

Memory location	Hex code	Mnemonic	Comments
0011	B6	LDAA	Sample output of sensor
0012	80 ⎫		by loading the accumulator
0013	01 ⎭	address	from A side data register.
0014	81	CMPA	Compare contents of accumulator
0015	0F	data	with set value (00001111).
0016	2C	BGE	Branch if greater than or equal to
0017	02	data	to location 001A.
0018	2D	BLT	Branch if less than
0019	07	data	to location 0021.
001A	C6	LDAB	Load accumulator B
001B	00	data	with (00000000).
001C	F7	STAB	Store the contents of
001D	80 ⎫		accumulator B in the B
001E	03 ⎭	address	side of PIA (data register).
001F	20	BRA	Branch always
0020	F0	data	to 0011 for another sample.
0021	C6	LDAB	Load accumulator B
0022	01	data	with (00000001).
0023	20	BRA	Branch always to
0024	F7	data	001C.

A flowchart for this program is shown in Fig. 10.10; this example illustrates the creation of a simple on/off controller using memory mapped operation.

10.5 Using the Zilog PIO

The PIO is representative of a device operating in a system having special input/output instructions. These opcodes assert a control line that activates only the input/output devices. In this way there is no response from the memory, and it is possible to simplify the address bus decoding. In the Zilog system each device decodes the least significant eight lines of the address bus. As a result, 256 addresses are available for input/output devices. By way of comparison and example, consider the PIO used for the same purpose as the PIA discussed in Section 10.3. Each PIO requires four addresses, because it also has two channels called A and B, and because each of these needs a control register as well as a data register. In the example the addresses are as follows.

A0	A side data register
A1	B side data register
A2	A side control register
A3	B side control register

Within the device there are several registers for control purposes. Some are only two bits wide and therefore the ultimate destination of data sent to the control addresses is determined by decoding the four least significant bits of the word. There are several

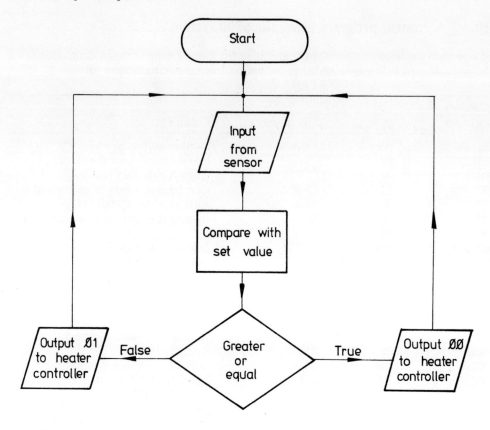

Fig. 10.10   A flowchart for the industrial process program

modes of operation and the one desired must be indicated by the first control word sent to the device during an initialisation sequence. If bit mode is selected the input/output register must be loaded next. This register is the equivalent of the DDR in the Motorola system and so each bit controls whether an individual data line on the peripheral side is to be an input or an output. For simple input or output the word written into the mode control register is all that is necessary; the bit direction register does not have to be set up.

The PIO control register allows four modes of operation. These are:

1)   simple input;
2)   simple output;
3)   A side byte bidirectional;
4)   bit mode.

Simple input/output is achieved by writing a control word into the control register. Only the two most significant bits of the control register determine how the port will operate and sending 00 to both these bits will arrange for simple byte output; 01 will result in simple byte input. The four least significant bits of the control register must be set to 1 in order that the word is recognised as being destined for the control register. The state of remaining bits is immaterial; see Figs. 10.11 (a) and (b).

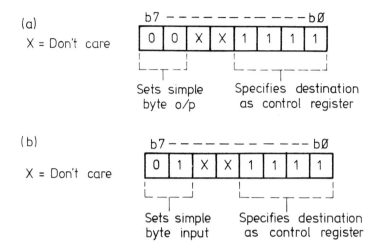

(a)

X = Don't care

b7 — — — — — — — — — b∅

| 0 | 0 | X | X | 1 | 1 | 1 | 1 |

Sets simple byte o/p

Specifies destination as control register

(b)

X = Don't care

b7 — — — — — — — — — b∅

| 0 | 1 | X | X | 1 | 1 | 1 | 1 |

Sets simple byte input

Specifies destination as control register

Fig. 10.11   The PIO control register

10.6   An initialisation routine using the Z80 system

The following program is an initialisation routine for simple input/output.

Memory location	Hex code	Mnemonic	Comments
∅D∅∅	3E	LD A	Load accumulator with
∅D∅1	7F	data	the control word for simple input
∅D∅2	D3	OUT	and send it to the A side
∅D∅3	A2	address	control register.
∅D∅4	3E	LD A	Load the accumulator with
∅D∅5	∅F	data	the control word for simple output
∅D∅6	D3	OUT	and send it to the B side
∅D∅7	A3	address	control register.

10.7   A control program using the Z80 system

The application discussed could be fulfilled by the program below, which would, as before, follow on from the initialisation routine.

Memory location	Hex code	Mnemonic	Comments
∅D∅8	DB	IN	Load accumulator from the data register
∅D∅9	A∅	address	of the A side.
∅D∅A	FE	CP	Compare with
∅D∅B	∅6	data	∅6.
∅D∅C	FA	JP	Jump if the result is negative

(continued overleaf)

Memory location	Hex code	Mnemonic	Comments
ØDØD	16 ⎫	address	to location ØD16.
ØDØE	ØD ⎭		
ØDØF	3E	LD A	Load the accumulator with
ØD10	00	data	hex 00.
ØD11	D3	OUT	Send 00 (or 01) to data register of the B side.
ØD12	A1	address	
ØD13	C3	JP	Jump unconditionally back to
ØD14	Ø8 ⎫	address	location ØDØ8.
ØD15	ØD ⎭		
ØD16	3E	LD A	Load the accumulator with
ØD17	Ø1	data	hex 01.
ØD18	C3	JP	Jump unconditionally back to
ØD19	11 ⎫	address	ØD11.
ØD1A	ØD ⎭		

10.8   The serial interface

Communications peripherals are designed to accept and transmit data in the form of 0s and 1s sent sequentially. The computer system moves data around as parallel words. What is needed as a go-between is a buffer shift register which can be loaded with a parallel word, and then clocked so that the pattern of its contents moves sequentially out through one end. This procedure deals with data transmission, but bidirectional data transfer with the peripheral is essential. The reverse action is needed in order to receive data; serial data is clocked into a buffer register, and when that register is full, its contents are made available as a parallel word.

Information interchange takes place in ASCII code. For asynchronous code, each character is preceded by start bit which signifies the beginning of the character, and concluded by two stop bits which signify the end. In the interests of error detection a parity system may also be employed. One bit of the signal, the **parity bit**, is not part of the character but is included within the start and stop bit frame; see Fig. 10.12. In an *even* parity signal, the parity bit is '0' if the number of character bits at logic '1' is even, but '1'

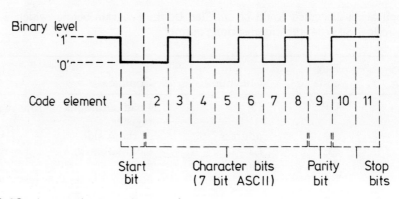

Fig. 10.12   An asynchronous character format

if this number is odd. The overall number of character bits and the parity bit at logic '1' is therefore always even. If in a character transfer, specified as even parity, the overall sum of 1s is odd, then an error has occurred in the transmission of that character. Many formats, or **protocols**, exist; for example, some systems use two stop bits per character and signals can have even, odd or no parity. To be sufficiently flexible a serial interface must be able to produce a range of signal protocols. Data can be transferred at a number of speeds and this, combined with the choice of signal protocol, indicates the need for full instructions about required performance to be sent to the interface. Such a control word is loaded into the device control register during initialisation. In addition to the factors already mentioned, it is essential for the required handshake procedure information to be included in the control word.

Keeping a note of the current status at any time is the function of the status flags register. Each bit of this register will indicate significant events during the interchange of data. For example, there are likely to be flag bits showing when the transmit or receive data buffer registers are empty, or perhaps when a parity error has occurred. Many useful indicators are possible, such as detecting that a word has been lost or that a word has been received without being properly framed by start and stop bits. The status register must be tested under program control before any of these conditions can be detected.

In summary, a serial interface will typically contain a minimum of four registers: an input data buffer, an output data buffer, a control word register and a status flags register. On the peripheral side it will have one input and one output data line. On the computer side it will have connections into the data bus, the address bus and the control bus; see Fig. 10.13. Some serial interfaces have the ability to operate synchronously, i.e. to exchange data without start and stop bits delineating characters. Also, considerable interrupt circuitry may be included, as described in Chapter 9. As in the case of the general-purpose parallel interface, there are many serial interface devices available. Just one is described in detail, and it serves as an example of the species.

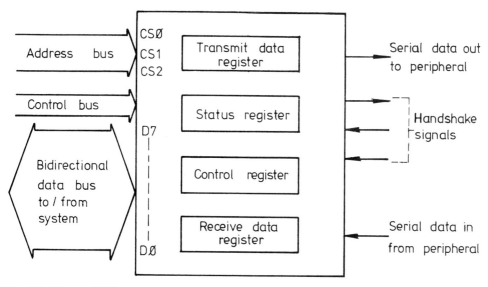

Fig. 10.13   An ACIA

10.9   Using the Motorola ACIA

The control and status registers share an address, as do the transmit and receive data registers. This is possible because it is only necessary to write to the control and transmit data registers, and to read the status and receive data registers; therefore the read/write decision determines the valid source of destination addressed. Since no reset line is provided, the first step in the initialisation is to clear all the registers in the device. This is done by writing a special master reset word into the control register. After this, a new control word sent to the same register will program the ACIA for a particular form of operation.

10.10   The ACIA control register

To understand the components of control words it is necessary to examine the control register. This is an 8-bit register in which the state of bits Ø and 1 determines the speed of sending the serial data. The clock frequency of the data shift register can be arranged to be a fraction of the ACIA clock, using the bit patterns shown in Table 10.2.

Table 10.2

b1	bØ	Data clock rate
0	0	Same as ACIA clock
0	1	ACIA clock ÷ 16
1	0	ACIA clock ÷ 64
1	1	Master reset word for device

   Serial data is usually transmitted or received at $\frac{1}{16}$ or $\frac{1}{64}$ of the clock rate. This is because in asynchronous transmission, at the beginning of each character, synchronism of the receiving device clock with the transmitting device clock is required so that any inaccuracies in the timing, or in the number of code elements, are detected. No other

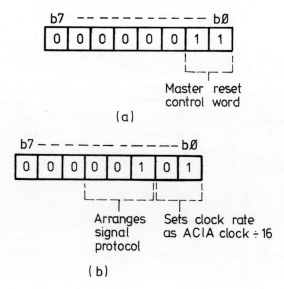

(a)

(b)

Fig. 10.14   Control register content for (a) master reset; (b) stated protocol

special measures are needed because the two clock oscillators should be sufficiently close in frequency that if synchronised at the beginning of the first element of code, their disparity should be negligible at a time 11 signal element periods later. The synchronising action takes place at the beginning of the start bit of the code, but a few cycles are necessary for adjustment. If the start bit is 16 or 64 clock periods this adjustment time is available.

Writing 11 into b0 and b1 is recognised as a master reset for the ACIA. This is necessary because as previously mentioned no reset control line connection to the control bus is provided. Resetting the ACIA, then, becomes a software rather than a hardware function; see Fig. 10.14(a).

Bits 2, 3 and 4 have written into them a 3-bit word which selects from the options concerning the number of data bits, the parity, and the number of stop bits required. The options available are shown in Table 10.3.

Table 10.3

b4,	b3,	b2	Protocol
0	0	0	7 bits, even parity, 2 stop bits
0	0	1	7 bits, odd parity, 2 stop bits
0	1	0	7 bits, even parity, 1 stop bit
0	1	1	7 bits, odd parity, 1 stop bit
1	0	0	8 bits, no parity, 2 stop bits
1	0	1	8 bits, no parity, 1 stop bit
1	1	0	8 bits, even parity, 1 stop bit
1	1	1	8 bits, odd parity, 1 stop bit

Bits 5 and 6 determine the operation of the handshaking control lines providing feedback from the peripheral; this will be discussed in more detail later.

The status of bit 7 affects the interrupt operation of the ACIA; see Chapter 9.

It is now possible to appreciate a suitable initialisation routine. In the examples, the addresses associated with the ACIA are as follows.

8010	Control register (write control line asserted)
8010	Status register (read control line asserted)
8011	Transmit data register (write control line asserted)
8011	Receive data register (read control line asserted)

10.11 An initialisation program for the Motorola ACIA

Memory location	Hex code	Mnemonic	Comments
0000	CE	LDX	Load the index register with the
0001	80 ⎫		address of the ACIA control
0002	10 ⎭	address	register.
0003	86	LDAA	Load the accumulator with the master reset
0004	03	data	control word.
0005	A7	STAA, X	Send it to the ACIA control
0006	00	data	register.
0007	86	LDAA	Load the accumulator with the

(continued overleaf)

Memory location	Hex code	Mnemonic	Comments
0008	05	data	control word*.
0009	A7	STAA, X	Send it to the ACIA control
000A	00	data	register.

*Sets signalling speed as clock frequency divided by 16 and arranges data transfer as 7-bit ASCII code with odd parity and 2 stop bits; see Fig. 10.14(b).

10.12　The status register

This 8-bit flags register is used to signal the condition of both receive and transmit data registers, as well as indicating the existence of a number of different error conditions. Additionally, information about the handshaking lines used with a standard modem is included. A **modem** is a peripheral device which permits interface with a telephone line system. The modem converts the 0s and 1s available on the serial data line into individual tones which can be passed over the telephone network. Incoming tones from remote modem/computer combinations are converted back to logic 0 and 1 levels by the receiving side of the modem, so that two-way data interchange can take place. Typical modem handshaking lines are: clear to send (CTS); ready to send (RTS); and data carrier detect (DCD). The CTS and RTS lines will control the data flow by the following method. When the sending ACIA flags 'ready to send', provided that the receiving modem has a clear receive data register, it flags 'clear to send' and the transfer of data is made. If the receiving modem has a full receive data register, it does not enable the 'clear to send' line and transfer is inhibited. The data carried detect line from the modem indicates when there is another modem seeking information interchange, although it has not yet begun to send data, or that the data carrier has been lost. The sending and receiving of data in this way is achieved under program control. Such a program must read and check the appropriate bits of the status register in order to fulfil its function.

The significance of the status register bits are as follows; see Fig. 10.15.

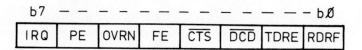

Fig. 10.15　The status register

b0 — Receive data register full flag
  '1'　Register full — IRQ also set, cleared when receive data register is read by CPU.
  '0'　Register has been read. The receive register data is not destroyed when read but b0 is clear. If $\overline{DCD}$ goes high, indicating loss of carrier (modem), b0 is clamped at 0 thus indicating receive register data is not current.
b1 — Transmit data register empty flag
  '1'　Transmit register empty.
  '0'　Transmit register full.
b2 — Data carrier detect flag
  '1'　No carrier from modem, IRQ bit 7 set unit CPU reads status and receive register.
b3 — Clear to send flag
  '1'　CTS line high — modem not ready for data.

'0'   CTS low — modem ready for data.
b4 — Framing error flag
   '1'   Indicates faulty transmission of a received character, in that data is improperly
      framed by start and stop bits.
   '0'   Received character correct.

Before new data can be sent to the transmit or receive data registers, the appropriate
status flag must be examined to ensure that the last data has been cleared. For example, if
character output to a peripheral is desired a program must be written to test the transmit
register status flag. In the event that the last character has not yet been fully clocked onto
the serial data line, the program must enter a wait loop, in which the status flag is
examined continually. When it confirms that the data register is clear, the new data may
be sent.

10.13 Output character routine without modem handshaking

Memory location	Hex code	Mnemonic	Comments
000B	C6	LDAB	Load accumulator B with
000C	41	data	an ASCII character.
000D	CE	LDX	Load the index register with
000E	80 ⎫	address	the address of the ACIA
000F	10 ⎭		status register.
0010	A6	LDAA	Load accumulator A with
0011	00	data	the status register contents.
0012	47	ASR	Shift data word right
0013	47	ASR	2 places to place transmit register
			empty flag in the carry bit.
0014	24	BCC	Test carry bit.
0015	FA	data	Branch back to 0010 if
			not set (enter wait loop);
0016	F7	STAA	otherwise store the contents of
			accumulator B in
0017	80 ⎫	address	the transmit data register.
0018	11 ⎭		

11
Some practical CPUs

The generalised CPU has been described in Chapter 6, and consideration will now be given to specific devices, particularly with regard to their power supplies, clock requirements and control lines. This will enable a comparison to be made between the different devices.

The earlier types of CPU required multiple power supplies, multiphase clocks and external control logic. This in turn meant they required a large number of support integrated circuits (ICs) to implement a working system. Specialised ICs, such as clock generators and system controllers were then developed in order to minimise the chip count.

The latest generation of CPUs require a single power supply and have on board clock circuitry which requires only the connection of a quartz crystal or resistor-capacitor (RC) network. This enables a very simple dedicated processor system to be built using just a few ICs.

11.1 The Motorola MC6802

The 6802 operates from a single 5 V power supply. It is an 8-bit parallel processor with a 16-bit address bus. The integrated circuit contains the same internal registers and accumulators that its predecessor the 6800 had, with the addition of an internal clock oscillator and 128 bytes of internal RAM located at addresses 0000 to 007F (hex). The first 32 bytes of the memory can be separately powered by batteries, enabling these locations to be retained during power down.

The block diagram of the internal architecture and its pin configuration are given in Figs. 11.1 and 11.2 respectively.

The CPU has two 8-bit accumulators which are used to hold operands and results from the ALU. Additionally there are three 16-bit registers: the program counter, the index register and the stack pointer. The condition codes register (flags register) has eight bits, of which only the six least significant bits are used.

11.1.1 System timing
A clock is used in order to time events within the CPU and the system in general. This clock may be externally generated using a frequency between 0.1 and 1.0 MHz or as is more usual by using the internal oscillator. Implementing the latter method would be achieved by connecting a quartz crystal as shown in Fig. 11.3.

The frequency of the crystal must be between 1 MHz and 4 MHz. The lower frequency limit is due to the use of internal dynamic memory, whereas the upper limit is determined by the operation of internal and external memory and other devices connected to the system busses. The 6800 family of processors work on a fetch-execute cycle in which one clock pulse period equals one machine cycle. If the internal oscillator is used, the crystal frequency is divided by four to produce the system clock. The timing for the rest of the system is provided by the 'E' signal. When 'E' is high, the data is taken

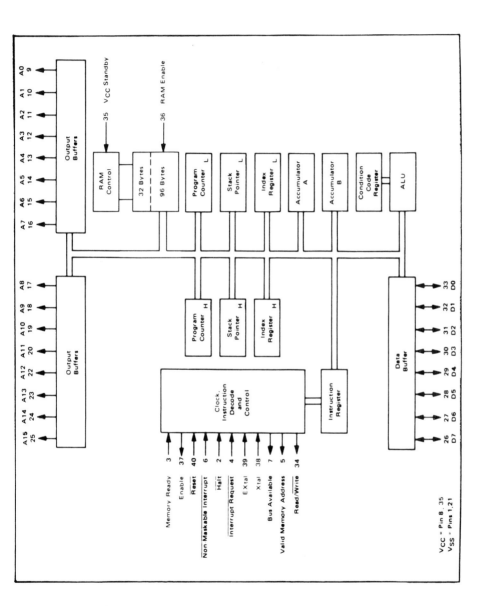

Fig. 11.1   6802 Expanded block diagram

PIN ASSIGNMENT

1	V_{SS}	Reset	40
2	$\overline{Halt}$	EXtal	39
3	MR	Xtal	38
4	$\overline{IRQ}$	E	37
5	VMA	$\overline{RE}$	36
6	$\overline{NMI}$	V_{CC} Standby	35
7	BA	$R/\overline{W}$	34
8	V_{CC}	D0	33
9	A0	D1	32
10	A1	D2	31
11	A2	D3	30
12	A3	D4	29
13	A4	D5	28
14	A5	D6	27
15	A6	D7	26
16	A7	A15	25
17	A8	A14	24
18	A9	A13	23
19	A10	A12	22
20	A11	V_{SS}	21

Fig. 11.2   6802 Pin out diagram

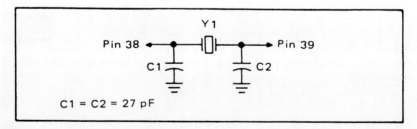

Fig. 11.3   Quartz crystal connection

into and transferred out of the CPU. When it is low, the CPU is carrying out internal operations.

The number of machine cycles taken to complete an instruction depends upon the addressing mode being used. Thus the extended mode, in which the data contents of a memory location must be fetched, will require more machine cycles than, say, the immediate mode, in which the data is held in byte 2 of the instruction. Figure 11.5 shows the fetch-execute cycle for the two-byte instruction using the immediate mode of addressing listed in Fig. 11.4.

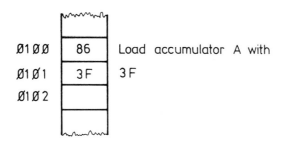

Fig. 11.4   A 6802 immediate mode instruction

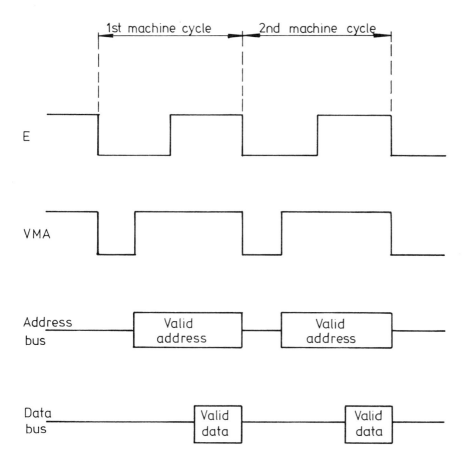

Fig. 11.5   Fetch—execute timing cycle

Referring to Fig. 11.5 the full cycle of operation is described below.

First machine cycle   The program counter address 0100 (hex) is placed on the address bus. The data from that location which is 86 (hex) is taken into the processor, and the program counter is incremented by one. The opcode is decoded during period 2 of the machine cycle. This decode operation informs the processor that the next byte is to be put into the accumulator A and also that there is no operation to be performed on the new accumulator contents.

Second machine cycle   The contents of the program counter 0101 (hex) are placed on the address bus and the data at that location which is 3F (hex) is transferred into the accumulator. The program counter is again incremented by one.

Next machine cycle   The opcode for the next instruction is fetched and decoded.

The total number of machine cycles contained in a program will indicate the total time of execution of that program. This enables a comparison of two or more programs to see which is faster, or to build up an accurate timing loop. Details of the number of machine cycles per instruction will be found in the machine code instruction set for the CPU.

11.1.2   Control and status lines
The eight control/status lines are divided into three distinct groups, each allowing the control or indicating the status of the following events:

i)   data transfer;
ii)   interrupt handling;
iii)   bus states.

All data transfer operations are controlled by two lines. The function of these lines is to determine whether it is a read or write action that is to take place, and in conjunction with the E control line the timing of that action. The two lines are as follows.

R/$\overline{\text{W}}$ Read or write. When high, this line indicates that the CPU desires to read the memory location whose address is on the address bus. When low, data is being written to that location.

VMA   Valid memory address. When high, this line indicates to a peripheral device that there is a valid address on the address bus. It becomes valid slightly before the processor starts a fetch cycle in order to allow the address, and therefore the data to stabilise, before the CPU reads the data.

Interrupt handling is controlled by three lines: Reset, NMI, IRQ. Their functions may be described as follows.

$\overline{\text{Reset}}$ This line is included in order to allow an orderly start up. When the line is momentarily taken low the processor is initialised and the addresses FFFE (hex) and FFFF (hex) are sequentially output on to the address bus. From these locations, a new address is built up, which gives the starting address of the program. Execution of that program begins immediately.

$\overline{\text{NMI}}$ Non-maskable interrupt. A low going edge on this line initiates the interrupt. The current instruction is completed and then the condition codes register, accumulators index register and program counter are pushed onto the stack. Addresses FFFC (hex) and FFFD (hex) are sequentially output onto the address bus; these locations contain the starting address of the NMI routine. At the end of the routine, the stack is pulled and the main program recommences at the point where it left off.

$\overline{\text{IRQ}}$ Interrupt request. When low, this line requests that an interrupt routine be called providing that the mask bit in the condition codes register is not set. The current instruction will be completed and the CPU register together with the return and address of the main program will be pushed onto the stack. The addresses FFF8 (hex) and FFF9 (hex) will then be output on the address bus. These locations contain the starting address of the IRQ routine. The stack is pulled at the end of the routine and the main program continues.

The remaining three lines are used either to control or to indicate the state of the busses. This allows the busses to be used by other devices, such as disc controllers, or to read from or write to the system memory independent of the CPU. Such an event is called a direct memory access (DMA).

Halt   When taken low, the process finishes its current instruction and then halts. The BA line goes high, VMA goes low, and the address bus contains the address of the next instruction. Tristating of the address bus, if required, should be done with suitable buffers.

BA   Bus available. This line indicates that the processor is either halted or in a wait state, and that the busses are available for use by other devices.

MR   Memory ready. When high the processor is running normally. When low, the 'E' signal may be stretched integer multiples of half periods. This allows the use of 'slow memory' in the system.

The two remaining CPU lines control the on-board RAM.

RE   RAM enable. When in the high state the 128 bytes of on-board RAM are enabled. When low they are disabled, thus allowing a larger off chip RAM to be used.

Vcc/Standby   This pin supplies the first 32 bytes of on-board RAM allowing a battery backup supply to be used. In the event of a power failure or when the system is switched off a limited number of bytes may therefore be retained.

11.2   The Intel 8085A

The 8085 is an 8-bit parallel processor with a multiplexed address bus. It requires a single +5 V power supply. The instruction set is 100% compatible with the 8080A but with an improved performance due to a higher frequency system clock. The block diagram of the internal architecture and its pin configuration are shown in Fig. 11.6 and Fig. 11.7 respectively.

The CPU has six 8-bit general purpose working registers which may be addressed singly or in pairs. It also has an 8-bit accumulator and a flags register. There are two 16-bit registers — the program counter and the stack pointer. The address bus is multiplexed with the address being split between the 8-bit address bus and the 8-bit data bus.

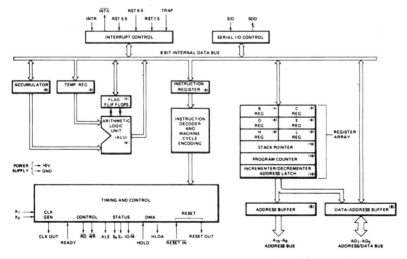

Fig. 11.6   8085 CPU functional block diagram (courtesy of Intel Corporation)

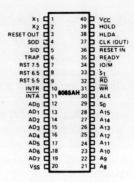

Fig. 11.7 8085 pin configuration

In order to distinguish between data and address the address latch enable (ALE) line is used.

One enhancement provided in the 8085 is the facility for serial input and output from the accumulator. The 8085 also has improved facilities for hardware interrupt operation.

11.2.1 System timing

The clock inputs of the 8085A may be driven by either a crystal, a tuned circuit (LC), a resistor capacitor network, or by an external source (see Fig. 11.8). The system clock period will be twice that of the input. The minimum clock frequency is 1 MHz for the fastest selected device.

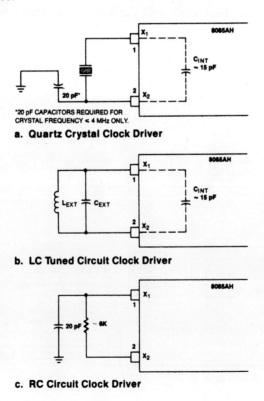

a. **Quartz Crystal Clock Driver**

b. **LC Tuned Circuit Clock Driver**

c. **RC Circuit Clock Driver**

Fig. 11.8 Clock driver circuits

Instructions in the 8085 take up to five machine cycles, depending upon the type of instruction. The machine cycles are labelled M1, M2 to M5, with each machine cycle taking from three to five clock cycles. The clock cycles are called T1, T2 to T5. Figure 11.9 shows the timing of the immediate mode instruction illustrated in Fig. 11.10.

Machine cycle M.1

Clock period T1   Programme counter contents, that is address 1010 (hex), is brought out onto the address bus lines AD0 to AD7 and A8 to A15. The low order 8-bit address would be latched into an external register.
Clock period T2   Read line ($\overline{\text{RD}}$) goes low. Programme counter contents containing low order 8-bit address is removed from lines AD0–AD7.
Clock period T3   Contents of memory location 1010 (hex), that is 3E (hex) in this example, is transferred along lines AD0–AD7 into instruction decoder of 8085 CPU.

Machine cycle M2

Clock period T1   Programme counter contents, that is address 1011 (hex), is brought out onto the address bus lines AD0 to AD7, and A8 to A15. The low order 8-bit address is latched into an external register.

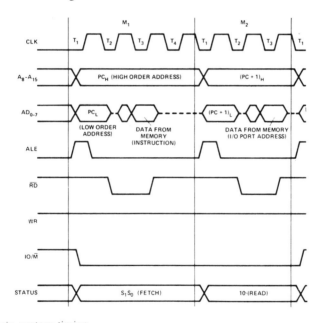

Fig. 11.9   Basic system timing

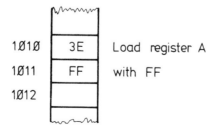

Fig. 11.10   An 8085 immediate mode instruction

Clock period T2   Read line ($\overline{\text{RD}}$) goes low. Programme counter contents containing low order 8-bit address is removed from line AD0–AD7.

Clock period T3   Contents of memory location 1011 (hex), that is FF (hex) in the example, is transferred along AD0 to AD7 and loaded into CPU Register A.

11.2.2   Control and status lines
The control and status lines of the 8085 can be separated into four functional groups. These groups are:

i)   data transfer;
ii)   machine cycle status information;
iii)   interrupt handling and reset;
iv)   bus control.

All data transfer operations that involve a read or write action to memory or I/O require the use of the following lines.

ALE — Address latch enable. This line pulses during the first clock state of a machine cycle and enables the lower half of the address to be latched off of the combined address/data bus (lines AD0–AD7).

$\overline{\text{RD}}$ — Read. When low, this line indicates that the selected memory or I/O peripheral device is to be read.

$\overline{\text{WR}}$ — Write. A low assertion on this line indicates that the data on the data bus is to be written to the selected memory location or I/O device.

READY — Ready. If the ready line is high during a read or write cycle, it indicates to the CPU that the memory and peripheral is ready to send or receive data. When low, the CPU waits an integer number of clock cycles until the ready line goes high, before completing the read or write cycle.

An indication of the CPU status and hence the part of the machine cycle being carried out is available by examining three lines — I0/$\overline{\text{M}}$, S1 and S0.

I0/$\overline{\text{M}}$, S1 and S0 — These lines indicate the machine cycle status according to Table 11.1.

Table 11.1

I0/$\overline{\text{M}}$	S1	S0	Status
0	0	1	Memory write
0	1	0	Memory read
1	0	1	I/O write
1	1	0	I/O read
0	1	1	Opcode fetch
1	1	1	Opcode fetch
	0	0	Halt

The lines became valid at the beginning of a machine cycle and remain throughout the cycle. S1 may be used as an advanced R/$\overline{\text{W}}$ status signal.

Interrupt handling is controlled by seven lines which are as follows.

INTR — Interrupt request. This line is used as a general purpose interrupt input which is enabled and disabled by software. If active, the programme counter will be inhibited from incrementing and a restart or call instruction may be used to execute the interrupt service routine.

INTA   Interrupt acknowledge. After an INTR is received this line goes low to
                    indicate that an interrupt has been accepted.
RST 5.5 ⎫   Restart interrupts. These three markable interrupt lines have an increasing
RST 6.5 ⎬   level of priority with RST 7.5 being the highest priority. When one of these
RST 7.5 ⎭   lines is asserted the CPU picks up the appropriate vector address as
                    described in Chapter 9, Section 9.7.
TRAP   Trap. The trap input is a non maskable interrupt. When activated the pro-
                    gramme counter is pushed onto the stack and the interrupt service routine
                    address is obtained from address 0024 (hex).
$\overline{\text{RESET IN}}$ Reset in. When low, this line initiates the power up restart sequence. The
                    restart vector is located at 0000 (hex).

The remaining two lines are used to control and indicate the state of the busses, thus
making them available for use by other devices.

HOLD   Hold. When this line goes high it indicates to the CPU that another
                    peripheral device requires the use of the data and address bus.
HLDA   Hold acknowledge. When high it indicates that the CPU has received the
                    HOLD signal and the busses will be free in the next clock cycle. The address
                    and data busses and also the $\overline{\text{RD}}$, $\overline{\text{WR}}$ and I0/$\overline{\text{M}}$ lines are all tristated.

11.3   The Zilog Z80

The Z80 has an 8-bit data bus and a 16-bit address bus. It requires a +5 V power supply
and a single-phase clock. The instruction set includes all 8080A instructions as a subset;
thus a machine code program written for the 8080A will run on a Z80, but not necessarily
vice versa.

   The block diagram of the internal architecture and its pin assignments are shown in
Figs. 11.11 and 11.12 respectively. There are two sets of 8-bit programmable registers

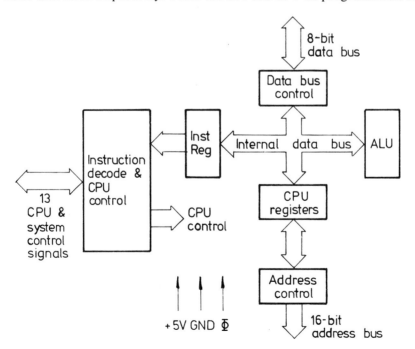

Fig. 11.11   Z80 CPU internal architecture (courtesy of Zilog (UK) Ltd)

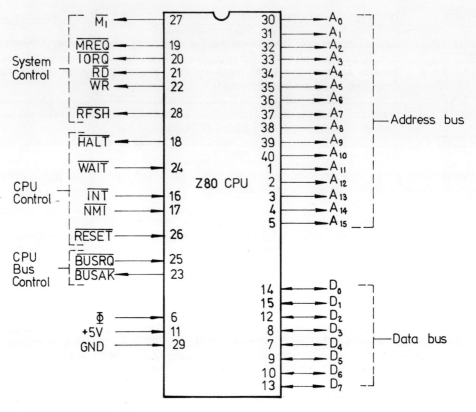

Fig. 11.12   Z80 pin assignment

and two program status words; only one set is active at a time. Four 16-bit registers are included; the stack pointer, the program counter and two index registers. The remaining 8-bit registers are the interrupt vector and the refresh register.

11.3.1 System timing

The clock input to the CPU may be provided by a simple oscillator generating a single-phase square wave. The clock will generally run at a frequency of between 1 MHz and 4 MHz. All Z80 machine cycles consist of three to six clock periods; up to six machine cycles are required to execute an instruction. The actual number of cycles is dependent upon the addressing mode being used. 'Wait' cycles may also be introduced into a machine cycle, but this again depends upon the instruction to be executed.

The timing of an instruction fetch sequence is shown in Fig. 11.13.

11.3.2 The control lines

There are three groups of control lines:

  i)   system control;
 ii)   CPU control;
iii)   bus control.

The six system control lines control the read/write operations. Their functions are as follows.

$\overline{\text{MI}}$ This line is used to indicate that the CPU is in an instruction fetch cycle.

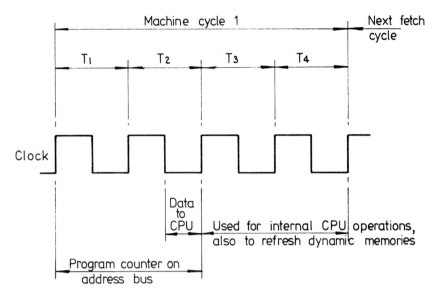

Fig. 11.13   Instruction fetch timing cycle

$\overline{MREQ}$ Memory request. This line indicates, when low, that there is a valid address on the address bus enabling a memory read or write operation.

$\overline{IORQ}$ Input/output request. When low, this line indicates that the lower half of the address bus holds a valid input/output address for a read or write cycle.

$\overline{RD}$ Memory read. This line indicates that the CPU wants to read a memory location or an I/O device.

$\overline{WR}$ Memory write. This line indicates that data on the data bus is valid.

$\overline{RFSH}$ Refresh. This line indicates to dynamic memory ICs that the current data on the address bus is a valid address. A refresh counter is included in the internal architecture of the CPU. This is incremented and placed on the seven least significant address lines during the periods T_3 and T_4.

There are five CPU control lines. Their functions are as follows.

$\overline{Halt}$ This indicates that the CPU has executed a software halt. NOPs (no operation) are executed in order to maintain the refresh cycle.

$\overline{Wait}$ This line flags the CPU that the addressed memory or I/O device is not ready for data transfer. The CPU introduces wait cycles within the memory cycle for as long as the wait line is low.

$\overline{Reset}$ This line initialises the CPU and resets the program counter to 0000 (hex); execution commences from this location, which will normally be the start of the ROM monitor.

$\overline{NMI}$ Non-maskable interrupt. When this line is taken low, the current instruction is completed and the program counter is pushed onto the stack. Program execution continues at 0066 (hex), the interrupt routine. Returning from the interrupt pulls the program counter from the stack, and execution of the main program continues from this address.

$\overline{IRQ}$ Interrupt request. This line is active when low and when the Z80 is in interrupt mode 0 acts in exactly the same way as in the 8080A. For further details see Chapter 9.

Two bus control lines are used as follows.

$\overline{\text{BUSRQ}}$ Bus request. This line flags the CPU to place its busses in the high impedance state to enable other devices to access the system busses.

$\overline{\text{BUSAK}}$ This line flags acknowledgement of $\overline{\text{BUSRQ}}$.

11.4   The MOS Technology 6502

This may be considered as an enhanced 6800 with no direct opcode compatibility. It has an 8-bit data bus and a 16-bit address bus. A single +5 V power supply is required, with

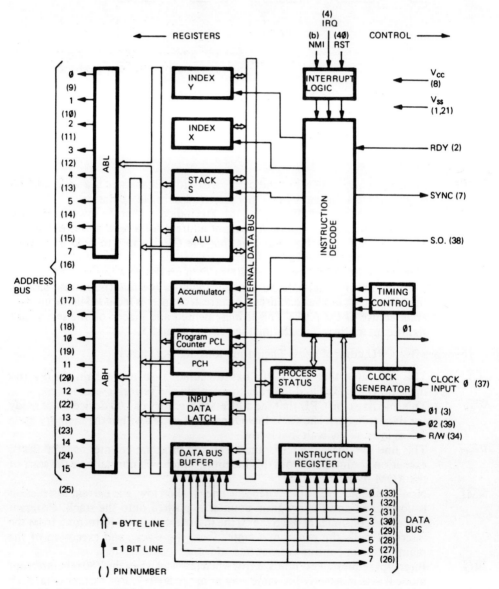

Fig. 11.14   MCS 6502 internal architecture (courtesy of Rockwell International)

an onboard oscillator which only requires the connection of an external crystal or an RC network. The internal architecture is shown in Fig. 11.14: this shows a single 8-bit accumulator, two 8-bit index registers, a 16-bit program counter, an 8-bit stack pointer and a status register. The pin configuration is shown in Fig. 11.15.

11.4.1   System timing
The onboard oscillator generates a two-phase non-overlapping clock, with a typical frequency of 1 MHz or 2 MHz. The period of the clock is equivalent to the period of the machine cycle; the fetching and decoding of instructions is carried out in a similar fashion to the same operations on the 6800.

11.4.2   The control lines
The control lines may be divided into two groups, one controlling each of the following types of operation:

i)   data transfer;
ii)   interrupts.

The data transfer lines are as follows.

R/$\overline{\text{W}}$ Read/write line. This allows control of the directions of data transfers. When high, data is being read; when low, data is being written to memory.

SYNC   This line is used to indicate when the processor is in an opcode fetch machine cycle.

RDY   Ready. When taken low, this line delays the execution of a fetch cycle, thus allowing the processor to operate with slow memories.

The three reset lines are as follows.

$\overline{\text{Reset}}$ When taken low, the processor is initialised and the program counter loaded sequentially with the addresses FFFC (hex) and FFFD (hex). From these addresses the starting address of the ROM monitor routine is built up. Program execution commences from that address.

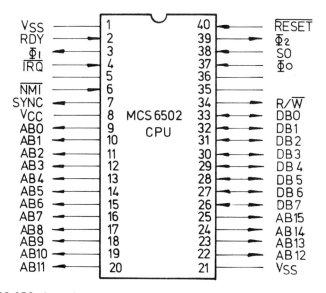

Fig. 11.15   MCS 650 pin assignment

$\overline{\text{NMI}}$ Non-maskable interrupt. On receipt of a low-going edge the current instruction is completed, the status register and program counter are pushed onto the stack and the program counter is loaded with the contents of FFFA (hex) and FFFB (hex). On returning from the interrupt the stack is pulled, and execution of the original program continues.

$\overline{\text{IRQ}}$ Interrupt request. When low, provided that the internal interrupt flag is cleared, the current instruction is completed. The status register and program counter are pushed onto the stack and the program counter loaded with the contents of FFFE (hex) and FFFF (hex). The stack is pulled on return from the interrupt and the main program continues.

11.5   A single-chip microprocessor

It is now possible to combine most of a microprocessor-based system into a single integrated circuit, and this is a measure of the advances being made in large-scale integration (LSI) technology. Figure 11.16 shows a typical single-chip system, the Intel 8048, which requires only a single +5 V power supply and a quartz crystal or RC network in order to produce a working system.

As well as the conventional CPU architecture, the system has on board the following components:

i)   a 1K × 8-bit ROM;
ii)   64 × 8-bit RAM;
iii)   3 × 8-bit I/O ports;
iv)   a timer counter.

The system may thus be used as a controller, cash register, etc., with very little external hardware.

11.6   The Intel 8086

The 8086 was the first 16-bit microprocessor to be developed by Intel and has the useful characteristic of being upward compatible with software designed for the 8-bit 8080 and 8085 processors. However, it will not execute machine code written for these earlier processors.

Use is made of the time divisioned multiplexed techniques to obtain the data and address information which uses the same set of 16 pins (AD0 to AD15). In addition there are a further four address lines which allow the possibility of addressing up to 1 million bytes of memory.

One of the unusual features of the 8086 is that some of the signal lines may have their functions reallocated according to the mode of operation selected. These are control signals which in one mode are selected to be suitable for use in a single processor system, whereas in the alternative mode they are changed to a new set of signals more suited for use in a multi-processor configuration.

A block diagram of the 16-bit processor is shown in Fig. 11.17 with the pin configuration of the 40 lead package shown in Fig. 11.18.

11.6.1   Architecture
The internal functions of the 8086 are divided into two major processing units which work asynchronously relative to one another. The first unit is the Bus Interface Unit (BIU) which carries out the functions related to instruction fetching and data read/write

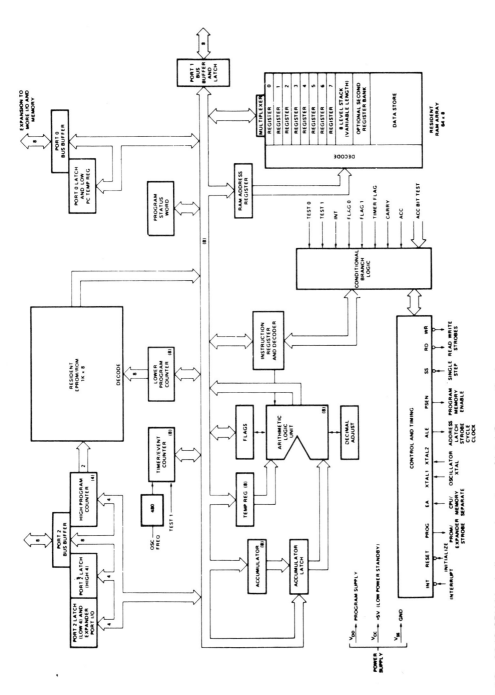

Fig. 11.16 8048 CPU block diagram (courtesy of Intel Corporation)

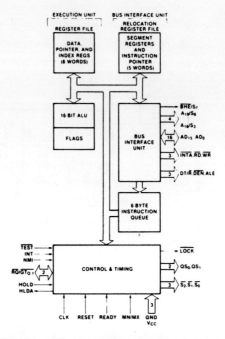

Fig. 11.17   Intel 8086 CPU block diagram (courtesy of Intel Corporation)

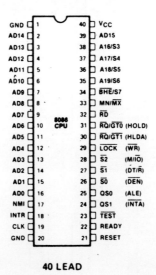

40 LEAD

Fig. 11.18   Intel 8086 pin configuration

operations. This unit also provides the basic bus control. The second major unit is the
Execution Unit (EU) which carries out the arithmetic and logic operations, as well as
handling the operands directly via the BIU during the fetch/execute cycle.

One of the purposes of the BIU is to pre-fetch from memory and stack up a queue of 6
bytes of instruction code ready for the execution unit. This instruction stream queuing
mechanism allows the BIU to keep the memory efficiently utilized and is effectively

creating an instruction pipeline which allows for faster and more efficient program execution.

There are four 16-bit registers which may be used as accumulators, but each register can also be treated as two 8-bit devices. In this mode the architecture takes on the familiar form of the 8080 and 8085 register set. In addition to the general purpose registers there are the normal 16-bit program counter, and stack pointer registers. The 8086 also has a 16-bit status flag register and a number of specialised registers associated with addressing modes and the special requirements of an effective 20-bit address.

The standard 8086 device operates with a 5 MHz CPU clock. Actual instruction execution time will vary according to the prevailing conditions in the CPU and the instruction queue in the BIU. In general, instructions will execute in some 600 ns to 4 μs depending upon whether memory access is required or not.

12
Semiconductor memories

Over the past few years considerable advances have been made in semiconductor memory technology. These have resulted in low-cost memory integrated circuits complementing the low-cost CPU chip. Although semiconductor memory devices are now universally used in microprocessor systems, an increasing amount of attention is being given to integrated memories based on magnetic bubble technology and charge-coupled devices (CCD).

Concentrating on semiconductor memory, microcomputers and nearly all microprocessor-based systems use both random access memory (RAM) and read only memory (ROM). These are usually made in the form of large-scale integrated (LSI) circuits. Considerable differences exist between the types of semiconductor memories available because of the wide range of LSI manufacturing processes possible. These differences manifest themselves in the form of power consumption, packing density, internal organisation, speed of operation, interface requirements, and methods of information storage.

12.1   Semiconductor memory technology

Construction of the integrated circuit memory chip can be carried out in a number of ways. Standard bipolar transistors (npn or pnp devices) may be used in integrated circuit form to produce the following types of logic: emitter-coupled logic (ECL); transistor-transistor logic (TTL); Schottky transistor-transistor logic (STTL); and current injection logic (I²L). Bipolar memory devices are fast in operation but consume more power per bit of storage than other types of memory. Within the family of bipolar memory devices, ECL is the fastest, followed by STTL.

The other main type of semiconductor device used for memory integrated circuits is the metal oxide silicon field-effect transistor (MOSFET). There are several types of MOSFET or MOS devices, such as PMOS (p-channel MOS), NMOS (n-channel MOS) and CMOS (complementary MOS). PMOS is the slowest and CMOS the fastest of the MOS memories, but all are somewhat slower than the bipolar types. The main advantages of MOS memories are low power consumption and high packing density. MOS transistors can be fabricated in a smaller space, thus allowing more bits to be stored in a given chip area.

12.2   Internal memory organisation

The address lines of an integrated circuit memory device will enable selection of one out of a number of memory locations. In some memory devices the selected storage location holds only one bit of information. Other devices are organised so that the selected location holds a group of binary digits, typically 4 or 8 bits. When characterising a specific memory device one of the factors quoted is the internal storage organisation.

Thus, a 1024 × 1-bit memory device means that the device has 1024 storage locations, each capable of holding 1 bit. This is generally referred to as a 1K × 1-bit memory. Other common memory organisations are 1024 × 8-bit (1K × 8), where each of the 1024 memory locations holds 1 byte, 4096 × 1-bit (4K × 1) and 16392 × 1-bit (16K × 1).

12.3   Memory operating speed

The operating speed of a memory device can be defined in a number of ways. Unfortunately no single standard method exists that enables an easy comparison to be made between the products of different manufacturers. Three of the more frequently-used parameters for specifying memory operating speed are: read cycle time (trcyc); write cycle time (twcyc); and access time (tacc). As a means of explaining these parameters the standard form of RAM chip shown in Fig. 12.1 will be used. This has read/write, data, address and chip select lines.

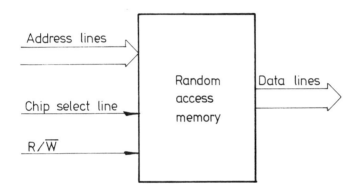

Fig. 12.1   Block diagram of simple RAM chip

12.3.1   Read cycle time (trcyc)
In either a ROM or RAM device a number of address lines are used to select a specific storage location within the IC. The minimum time possible between one address being set up on the address lines and a new address applied to the same lines is referred to as the read cycle time. In other words it is the minimum time required between successive read operations.

12.3.2   Access time (tacc)
After the correct address is supplied to the chip address lines during a read operation, a delay will occur before the data stored in the addressed location appears and settles down on the data output lines. This can be more succinctly described as the time from the start of the read cycle to the time when the memory data outputs are valid.

12.3.3   Read cycle timing diagram
Figure 12.2 shows a timing diagram indicating cycle and access time characteristics during a read operation. It is conventional for address and chip select line waveforms to show both possible transitions. This is because at the changeover some of the lines will be going from a low to high value, while other lines are moving in the opposite direction.

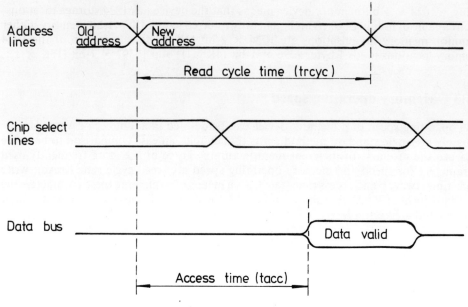

Fig. 12.2   Timing diagram for read cycle

12.3.4   Write cycle time (twcyc)
This is the minimum time that will be taken between successive write operations. In RAM devices, write cycle time is very often the same value as the read cycle time.

12.3.5   Write cycle timing diagram
In the write cycle timing diagrams of Fig. 12.3 it is assumed that the input data is stable for the requisite minimum length of time (another memory parameter) and the write operation is obtained by taking the R/$\overline{\text{W}}$ line low.

12.4   Types of semiconductor memory

The two main types of semiconductor memory can be split into a number of smaller categories. Figure 12.4 gives an indication of the general breakdown within each type.

When information in the form of programs and data has to be stored and changed, random access memory will be used. Permanent storage of information requires the use of read only memory. The different categories of ROM are mainly an indication of the way that information is permanently held in the integrated circuit.

Both static and dynamic RAMs are **volatile** stores, i.e. when electrical power is removed from the chip, information previously held is lost. In the case of dynamic RAM, stored information will also be lost if an operation called refreshing does not periodically take place. Some RAMs, particularly those constructed from MOS devices, use so little power in the standby mode that a back-up battery supply can be used to hold the information for days in the event of a mains power failure.

12.4.1   Random access memory
Random access memory, sometimes known as **read-write** memory (RWM) can come in two basic forms; static and dynamic. A simple **static** RAM chip consists of a large number of flip-flops or bistable elements. Each flip-flop stores one bit of binary

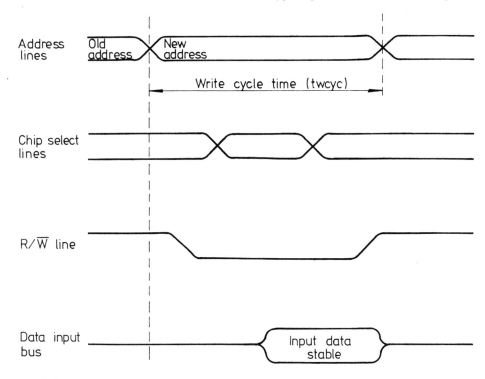

Fig. 12.3   Timing diagram for write cycle

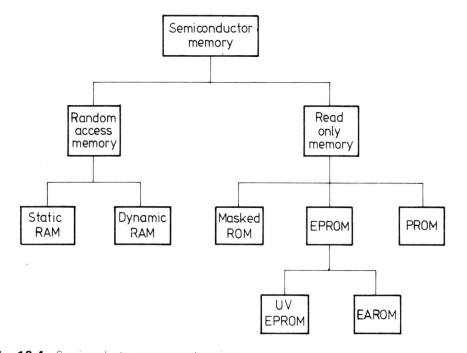

Fig. 12.4   Semiconductor memory categories

information and is constructed in integrated circuit form from either bipolar or MOS devices. The overall circuitry necessary to achieve a read and write operation can become quite complex. This tends to limit static RAMs to a storage capacity of about 4K bits per chip.

In the case of **dynamic** RAM, binary information is not held in a flip-flop element but is stored as an electrical charge on the gate capacitance of a MOS transistor. Since these capacitors are not perfect, the charge will leak away and the information be lost unless the capacitor is periodically replenished. This periodic recharging is called **refreshing** the memory. Refreshing can be achieved in several ways depending on the type of device; but in general the procedure consists of cycling through each address location at least once every 2 ms. In most cases external circuitry is required for the refresh operation which has to be synchronised with the CPU read and write cycles. Some dynamic memories have on-chip automatic refresh circuits which in application make them look like static memories.

Dynamic RAMs use only a small number of MOS transistors to store one bit of information and can therefore produce a higher packing density and lower cost per bit than static RAMs. Dynamic memory chips capable of storing upto 256K bits are now available.

A general comparison of the characteristics of a number of common RAM types is given in Table 12.1.

Table 12.1   Comparison of RAM characteristics

| Type | Organisation (words × bits) | Access time (ns) | Cycle time (ns) | Power dissipation (mW) | |
				Operating	Standby
ECL	1024 × 1	30	40	520	520
Static NMOS	1024 × 1	450	450	150	150
Static CMOS	1024 × 1	100	100	50	0.1
Dynamic NMOS	4096 × 1	200	200	490	2.6

12.4.2   Single-chip 1K × 1-bit RAM

The block diagram of Fig. 12.5 shows the internal structure of a 1K × 1-bit static RAM. The 1024 memory locations are organised into a 32 × 32 memory element array. Selection of any one of the 1024 memory locations requires ten address lines because $2^{10} = 1024$. According to the 5-bit address code placed on the lines A0–A4, one of the 32 lines from the row decoder circuit will be selected. The same procedure takes place in the column decoder circuit based on the binary code fed to the address lines A5–A9. From this row/column coordinate one of the 1024 cells will be selected.

Provided that the chip select (CS) line is held low, a read or write operation can now take place on the selected memory location. When the read/write (R/$\overline{\text{W}}$) line is high, the content of the memory location is fed to the data output line. A logic 0 on the R/$\overline{\text{W}}$ line initiates a write operation which causes the logic level on the data input line to be stored in the selected memory location.

12.4.3   Read only memory

The term 'read only memory' is applied to a memory circuit where binary information is permanently stored for later retrieval. This information is not lost when the power is removed; the memory is thus **non-volatile**. ROMs can be divided into three types which differ as to how information is programmed into the memory location.

Masked programmed ROM   This type of ROM has the program written into it as the IC

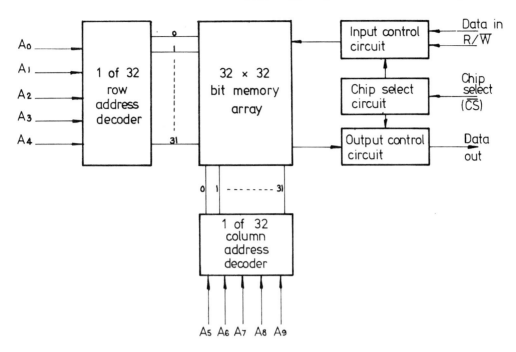

Fig. 12.5   1024 × 1-bit static RAM

is being made. Initially a blank memory is fabricated using standard semiconductor manufacturing techniques. Then a photographic negative called a **mask** is used to set the individual memory elements to certain binary values. As a special mask must be produced for each different set of information to be stored, this type of ROM is only suitable for volume production. Only then can the high initial cost of producing the mask be spread over a large number of units.

Programmable ROM (PROM)   A PROM can be programmed by the user after purchase. Each memory bit element in the PROM contains a nichrome or silicon link that acts as a fuse. The user can selectively 'burn out' or 'blow' these fuses by applying pulses of current to appropriate pins of the IC. A memory element with an unblown fuse stores a 1 and a blown fuse stores a 0. The programming process is irreversible, so it must be right first time.

PROMs are capable of high operating speeds, but consume a relatively large amount of power. However, since they are non-volatile, they can be switched off when not being accessed.

Erasable programmable ROM (EPROM)   These are memory devices that can be programmed, erased and then reprogrammed by the user as often as required. The programming procedure is similar to the PROM type, with commercially-available EPROM programmers reducing the programming time to a matter of a few minutes.

Two methods of erasing the bit pattern stored in an EPROM are currently available. In a UV-EPROM, information is stored as a charge in a MOSFET device. The information can be erased by flooding the chip with ultraviolet light through a quartz window. Following this process the complete memory has been erased, and a new bit pattern can then be entered.

In the electrically alterable PROM (EAPROM), normally referred to as an EAROM, the contents of the complete memory can be erased by applying voltages to appropriate pins of the integrated circuit.

The erasing process is fairly slow, and often requires voltages and circuit techniques that are not commonly found in normal logic circuitry.

A sample comparison of read only memories is shown in Table 12.2.

Table 12.2   Comparison of ROM characteristics

Type	Organisation (words × bits)	Access time (ns)	Cycle time (ns)	Power dissipation (mW)
ECL	32 × 8	20	40	500
NMOS	4096 × 1	150	400	400
CMOS	1024 × 8	150	400	200

12.4.4   Single-chip 1024 × 8-bit UV-EPROM

The block diagram of Fig. 12.6 shows the internal structure of a UV-EPROM. Each of the 1024 addressable memory locations stores 8 bits of information; the locations are

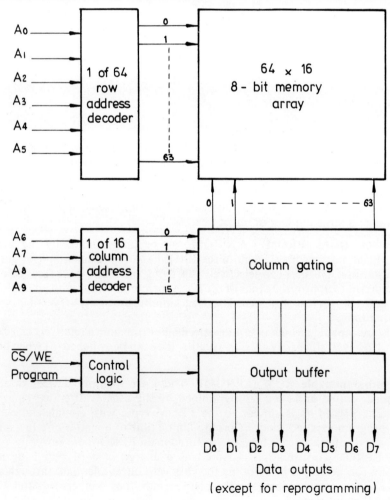

Fig. 12.6   1024 × 8-bit UV EPROM

arranged in a 64 × 16 array. The address lines A0–A5 select one of the 64 rows and the lines A6–A9 select one of the 16 columns. The row/column coordinate produced therefore selects one 8-bit memory location. When the chip select ($\overline{CS}$) line is taken low, the byte of stored information is fed via the column gating circuit to the output buffers.

When reprogramming the EPROM, the memory is first wiped clean by exposure to ultraviolet light. The address of the first memory location is set up on the address lines, the byte to be stored is then applied to the data lines and the $\overline{CS}$/WE line taken high — write enabled.

The write action takes place when a voltage pulse of 12–30 V (depending on memory type) is applied to the program terminal for between 0.1 ms and 1 ms. Following this, the next storage location is selected, new data applied, and the procedure repeated. After the full program has been entered, the complete operation is repeated a number of times to ensure that the program has been correctly stored.

12.5   Expansion of memory word size

Very often the storage capacity of each location in a memory integrated circuit is inadequate for the system. For instance, throughout this book an 8-bit data word length is used, but many memory integrated circuits only store 1 bit or 4 bits at each address. To overcome this problem, several memory chips must be combined in order to produce the required word size.

As an example, consider the typical 256 × 4-bit static RAM shown in Fig. 12.7. Each of the 256 memory locations is selected by an 8-bit address, with each location holding a 4-bit word. Four common data input/output lines are available, with the $R/\overline{W}$ line controlling the read/write action. One chip select line is also included.

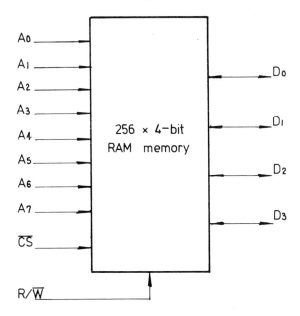

Fig. 12.7   256 × 4-bit static RAM

If an 8-bit word size is required, then two 256 × 4-bit identical RAMs can be combined. Such an arrangement is shown in Fig. 12.8.

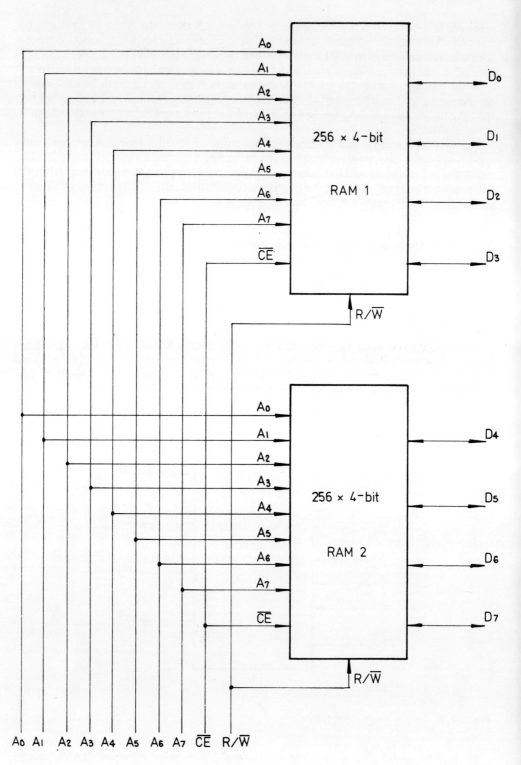

Fig. 12.8   256 × 8-bit two-chip RAM

With an 8-bit address applied to the common lines A0–A7, and the $\overline{CS}$ line held low, one 4-bit memory location is selected in RAM 1 and a similar location in RAM 2.

If the read line is high, then the contents of RAM 1 are applied to data lines D0–D3 as the least significant 4 bits of the 8-bit word, and the contents of RAM 2 appear on D4–D7 as the most significant 8 bits.

The same basic configuration can be used for other memory circuit organisations. If a number of 1K × 1-bit memory circuits (see Fig. 12.5) are to be used for storing an 8-bit word length, then a total of eight integrated circuits would be required. Each of the ten address lines to a memory chip would be connected to the corresponding lines of the other seven circuits. The single data input/output line of each chip is used to form an 8-bit data bus.

12.6 Expansion of memory capacity

Besides increasing the word size by combining a number of memory circuits, it may be necessary to increase the overall memory capacity. We have seen in Section 12.5 how two 256 × 4-bit memory chips can be combined to provide storage of 256 8-bit words. If more than 256 bytes of storage are required then capacity can only be increased by combining more memory circuits. The arrangement shown in Fig. 12.9 illustrates how a 1024 × 8-bit memory capacity can be produced.

The basic RAM is a 256 × 8-bit device that can be either a single integrated circuit or two 256 × 4-bit devices. For the latter system, the devices would be combined in the manner previously described. Address lines A0–A7 are common to all four RAMs. A binary address set up on A0–A7 would therefore select the same memory locations in RAM 0, RAM 1, RAM 2 and RAM 3. As the data lines D0–D7 are common, four 8-bit words would be applied simultaneously during a read cycle to the common data bus. To prevent this type of non-selective read and write action, a chip select line is used; some manufacturers call this a **chip enable** line. Two further address lines A8 and A9 are used and decoded in such a manner that at any one time only one of the RAM chip select ($\overline{CS}$) lines is low. One result of this arrangement is that according to the 10-bit address on lines A0–A9 only one 256 × 8-bit chip will be selected, allowing a read/write operation to take place on that RAM device only.

Table 12.3 Chip select address decoder truth table

Address lines		Decoder outputs				Comments
A8	A9	0	1	2	3	
0	0	0	1	1	1	RAM 0 selected
1	0	1	0	1	1	RAM 1 selected
0	1	1	1	0	1	RAM 2 selected
1	1	1	1	1	0	RAM 3 selected

The truth table of the decoder circuit necessary for chip selection is shown in Table 12.3. A possible logic gate circuit using NAND and NOT gates is illustrated in Fig. 12.10.

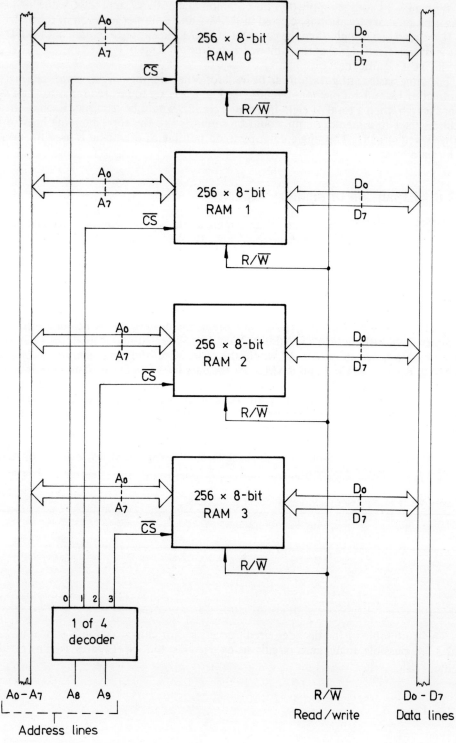

Fig. 12.9   1024 × 8-bit RAM using four chips

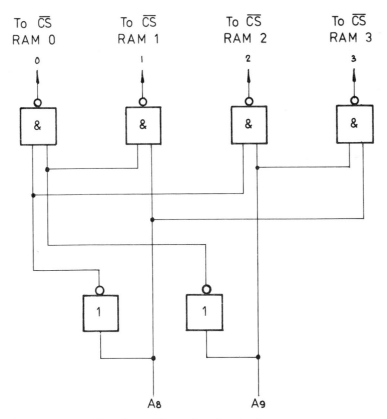

Fig. 12.10 Logic gate chip select address decoder circuit

12.7 Memory block address allocation

In the standard 8-bit microprocessor system a 16-bit address bus provides 65 536 (64K) addressable memory locations. In hexadecimal, this address ranges from 0000 to FFFF and constitutes the total memory space. When a microprocessor-based system or micro-computer is being designed, a decision will have to be made on how the memory space is to be allocated.

When the 6802 MPU is reset, the program counter automatically goes to FFFE to pick up a vector address. There must therefore be at least some ROM in this memory area to direct the MPU to another part of the memory space.

A reset operation in the 8085/Z80 system causes the program counter to go to 0000 (hex), and so in this case some ROM must be placed at the low end of the memory space. These points are illustrated by Fig. 12.11 which shows totally different memory space allocations for two microcomputer systems.

If a block of memory, either RAM or ROM, is to be situated in a specific area of the memory space, then decoding of the 16-bit address bus is required. As an example, consider a 4K × 8-bit block of memory constructed on a printed circuit board which requires connection to the system address and data busses.

To address any one of the 4096 memory locations within that memory block, twelve address lines are required (2^{12} = 4096). In hexadecimal form this will represent an address in the range 000 to FFF. Connection of the twelve address lines to the low-order lines of the full address bus is shown in Fig. 12.12.

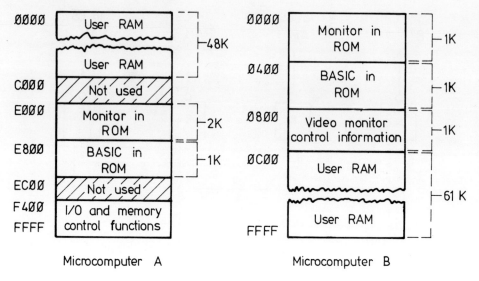

Fig. 12.11 Comparison of microcomputer memory space allocation

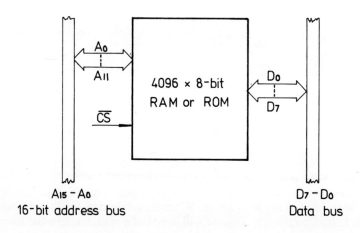

Fig. 12.12 Address line connection for 4K memory

However, this basic arrangement allows a number of 16-bit addresses to select a specific memory location within the 4K memory board. For example, the first memory location in the 4K block has an address 0000 0000 0000 (ØØØ hex); but the 16-bit addresses ØØØØ, 1ØØØ, 2ØØØ, 3ØØØ up to FØØØ (hex) will all be capable of selecting this location. To ensure that only one 16-bit address selects a memory location within the 4K block, the high-order 4 bits of the address bus must be decoded and used to control the chip select line. This arrangement is shown in Fig. 12.13.

If the 4K block of memory is to be located in the memory space from BØØØ to BFFF then the chip select line must only be taken low when the binary number 1011 (B hex) is present on the address lines A15–A12. A logic gate decoder circuit capable of providing this control function is shown in Fig. 12.14.

In a commercially-produced memory board, address bus decoding facilities are normally provided which can be set up by means of links or miniature switches. Figure

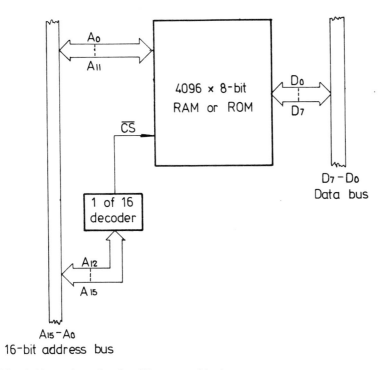

Fig. 12.13 Address decoding for 4K memory block

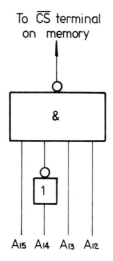

Fig. 12.14 Decoding circuit for 4K memory block

12.15 shows how decoding the most significant four address lines can position a 4K block of memory anywhere within the 64K memory space.

To position an 8K block of memory within the memory space, only three of the high-order address lines (A13–A15) need to be decoded. For a smaller block, such as 1K, 6 address lines A10–A15 are required for chip select decoding.

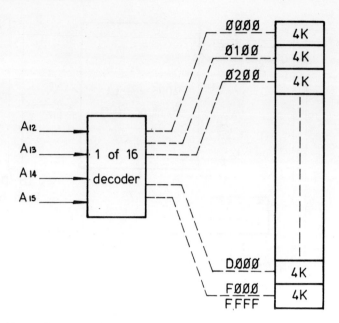

Fig. 12.15 Address allocation within memory space

12.8   Use of bus drivers

The address bus carries signals that originate in the CPU. Most CPUs are MOS devices where each address line can only supply the load for one bipolar TTL logic gate. Typically, logic gates and specific decoders are TTL devices because of the speed of operation and easy availability. In a memory system where more than one TTL logic gate is to be connected to the high-order address lines, buffering circuits must be placed between the CPU address line outputs and the memory board decoding circuit. A typical bus buffer or driver is shown in Fig. 12.16.

When the control line is high the output logic level of the buffer circuit follows the input. But when the control line is held low, the output stage of the device goes into an 'off' or high impedance state, effectively isolating the buffer circuit from any common bus line connected to its output.

Although the low-order address lines usually have a number of memory chips connected to them, buffering is not always required. This is because RAM and ROM

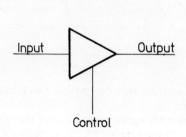

Input	Control	Output
0	1	0
1	1	1
0	0	High impedance
1	0	High impedance

Fig. 12.16   Three-state bus driver

circuits are normally MOS devices which have a substantially lower loading effect. If, however, a large number of memory circuits are used, or bipolar devices are employed, bus buffering will also be required on the low-order address lines.

For the same reason, the CPU data lines may also require buffering if memory and interface circuits represent more than one TTL load.

12.9 Full microprocessor-based system

The interconnections necessary between various devices to implement a simple 8-bit microprocessor-based system are shown in Fig. 12.17. The system consists of a CPU or MPU chip, 256 bytes of RAM, 4096 bytes of ROM, and an input/output unit for controlling a peripheral device.

The CPU uses a single-phase external clock, and also has connected to it a simple restart circuit that asserts the reset line at switch-on. Any reset operation causes the program counter to be loaded with the address of a reset vector location situated within the ROM. The main program will be permanently stored in ROM, while any data fed in from the peripheral device or produced during execution of the main program will be temporarily held in RAM. Interrupt control is used for data transfer between the data register of the input/output unit and the CPU. Handshaking facilities also exist between the peripheral device and the input/output unit.

Of the 16-bit address bus, eight lines (A0–A7) are required to address any one of the 256 bytes of RAM, and twelve lines (A0–A11) required for the 4096 bytes of ROM. In addition the input/output unit has two addressable devices within its chip. One of these is the data register, used for interfacing the system data bus with the data lines going to the peripheral. The second addressable device is the control register, which will enable the general input/output unit to be programmed for a specific type of data transfer operation.

Chip select decoder circuits fed from some of the high-order address lines will be necessary in order to prevent incorrect addressing taking place. The actual decoding arrangement will depend on the address allocation for the ROM, RAM and input/output device. For the system being discussed these addresses are as follows:

RAM	0000 to 00FF (hex)
I/O control register	E000 (hex)
I/O data register	E001 (hex)
ROM	F000 to FFFF (hex)

Using these addresses, one possible method of decoding for chip selection is given in Table 12.4.

Table 12.4 Address line decoding

Device	Binary address	Chip selection decoding
	A_{15}　　　　　　　A_0	
RAM	0000 0000 0000 0000 0000 0000 1111 1111	Selected when A13 and A12 both low
I/O control reg	1110 0000 0000 0000	Selected only when A13 high. A12 and A0 low
I/O data reg	1110 0000 0000 0001	Selected only when A13 and A0 high. A12 low
ROM	1111 0000 0000 0000 1111 1111 1111 1111	Selected only when A13 and A12 both high

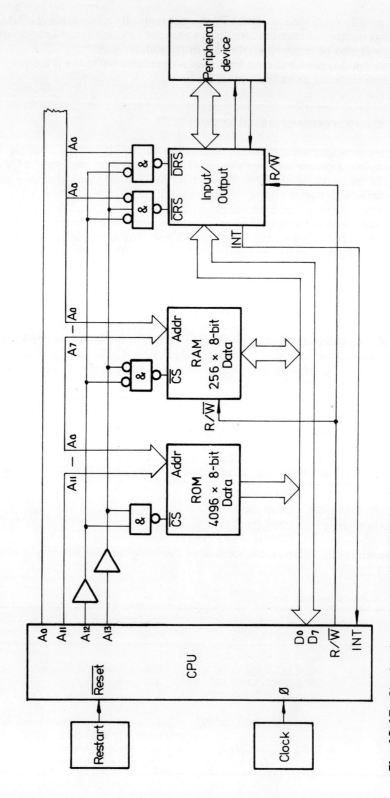

Fig. 12.17   Simple microprocessor-based system

Decoding address lines A12 and A13 means that a number of address combinations could select a specific memory location within RAM or ROM. For example, the first memory location in RAM is given the hex address 0000; but hex code addresses 4000, 8000 and C000 will also select this location. The reason for this is that in all four addresses, the lines A12 and A13 are low and will therefore cause the RAM to be selected or enabled. However, the three addresses that cause false selection of the RAM are all relating to parts of the memory space that are not being used in the system being considered. This, in turn, means that these addresses will not normally occur in any part of the main program, and so will not cause false chip selection. Under these circumstances, the proposed decoding circuits for chip selection are adequate for a system with the memory space address allocation described previously.

Because of the loading effects of the decoding circuits on the A12 and A13 address lines, a bus buffer device is connected to each line. Although not shown in Fig. 12.17 it may also be necessary to place a bus buffer on the A0 line. This is because of the decoding associated with addressing either the control or data register of the input/output unit.

13
Microcomputer firmware and software

13.1 The ROM monitor

As explained earlier, a machine code program is a series of instruction and data bytes. How is it possible to enter such a program into the memory of a microcomputer system?

At the instant of switch-on, the memory will contain random data which would be of no significance to the processor even if the processor had the ability to read the memory. A newly switched-on microcomputer is like an empty brain: it does not even know how to communicate.

Traditionally, computers were given the intelligence to communicate with the user by loading an **operating system program** into the memory and then running it. All the loading had to be done by hand, specifying a memory location by using keyswitches to set each bit of the address bus to 0 or 1 and specifying the word that is to be written into memory by using keyswitches to set each line of the data bus to 0 or 1.

This is an extremely tedious process, and microsystems avoid it by providing the operating system in read only memory (ROM). A program held in read only memory is called **firmware**; such a program is never forgotten, and as soon as the system is switched on the processor is automatically made to fetch and execute the program stored in ROM. This program gives the system the ability to communicate, and is called the **monitor**.

As well as bringing the system under the user's control, most monitor programs allow a variety of functions concerned with entering and correcting user programs in random access memory.

Unfortunately, there is no standard structure or format for monitors, and the general level of sophistication is quite variable. However, they all provide the essential capability to examine the contents of a memory location. When told to do so, the monitor will cause the appropriate byte to be read and output to the display, usually in hexadecimal form. Any two-digit hexadecimal number keyed in subsequently will replace the previous contents. The more sophisticated monitor programs will include other commands.

Typically the following command functions might be included.

1) Memory change or examine. This enables the user to change the contents of any memory location; or to move in single steps through the memory in order to check the instruction or data resident in each location.
2) List X, Y. Lists the memory contents between addresses X and Y.
3) Punch X, Y. Outputs data between X and Y via a magnetic tape interface; or punches a paper tape of the memory contents between X and Y.
4) Load. Loads the memory from a magnetic tape via a tape interface; or loads the memory from a punched tape read by the peripheral tape reader.
5) Execute. Goes to the user's program start location and executes the program.
6) Breakpoint. Causes the program to execute only up to the location specified.

In addition to commands, it is possible to include within the monitor various subroutines that are useful to the user. The following functions fall into this category.

a)   Accept 4 hex digits and load the index register with them.
b)   Accept 2 hex digits from an input device and store them in the accumulator.
c)   Accept a character from a terminal, and store it in the accumulator.
d)   Print a space.
e)   Print a message until a terminator character is read.
f)   Output 2 hex digits to a terminal device.
g)   Output 4 hex digits to a terminal device.
h)   Output a character to a terminal device.

Any of these can be called by using a 'jump to subroutine' instruction. The use of such subroutines represents a considerable economy of the space required in RAM for the user's program.

The use of a monitor will be described with the aid of an example. Because monitors differ so much, readers intending to work through the exercises and programs in this book are strongly urged to familiarise themselves with the commands and routines available within their own monitors and also to become familiar with operational aspects.

The monitor used in the example is intended to be a guide to the type of procedures that will be encountered.

13.2   Using the monitor

13.2.1   The procedure for loading a program

Switch on the processor and VDU, teletype or display (if separately powered). The system should respond with a prompt. A **prompt** is a symbol which appears on the display. Any character may be used; for example, in this case it is '*'.

The monitor is now in **command mode** and is waiting to be told what to do. The first step in loading a program is to use the memory examine, 'M', command to decide the address in memory at which the program is to start. The example program will begin at location 0100 (hex). The memory change command must now be used to insert the first instruction into the location 0100. A single letter constitutes the command and to achieve the objective the following must be keyed into the system.

	Action	Comments
Key in	M0100	This command examines the memory location 0100.
Monitor's		The computer returns the contents of location 0100, i.e.
response	0100 5E	5E.
Key in	space	This informs the monitor that the contents are to be changed.
Key in	86	The first byte of the program (86) is loaded into the location.

If the display is a VDU or teletype the following series of events will have been produced.

```
*M 0100
0100 5E 86
0101 0D
```

Note that after the byte 86 was written into 0100 the computer returns with the contents of the next location (0101), which is 0D. With an LED display, of course, only the most recent line will appear. Also, some monitors require a specific command to step to the next memory location. To input the second byte of the program the following sequence must be keyed in.

	Action	Comments
Key in	space	Monitor informed that the contents of Ø1Ø1 are to be changed.
Key in	56	The new contents of Ø1Ø1 are to be 56 (hex), and this is written up.
Monitor's response	Ø1Ø2 FD	

Continue in the same way with the rest of the program until the last byte has been entered. If a mistake is made in entering data, there is usually a command to enable backward steps in the memory. If the memory location examined is not to be changed a character that is interpreted as a forward step should be input instead of 'space'. The following sequence is an example of this procedure.

	Action	Comments
Key in	M Ø1ØØ	
Response	Ø1ØØ 86	
Key in	/	Step to next location without changing Ø1ØØ.
Response	Ø1Ø1 56	

This stepping operation should be repeated until all the memory locations holding the program have been checked. If a location is found to have incorrect contents, key in 'space' instead of '/' and enter the correct hexadecimal data.

13.2.2   Running a program
Make sure that the monitor is in the command mode. If it is not, restart the monitor program by pressing the system reset button. Some monitors recognise a character such as 'carriage return' as an instruction to return to command mode. This is indicated by the prompt once again appearing on the display. Assuming that the command letter for program execution is 'G', then:

	Action	Comments
Response	*	Monitor command mode restored.
Key in	G Ø1ØØ	This causes the program to commence execution.
Response	*	Program finished, monitor returns to command mode.

This last action of returning to monitor command mode can be achieved by making the last instruction of the program an unconditional jump to the beginning of the monitor program. An alternative is to conclude the program with a halt instruction to the processor. Control is then regained by pressing the system reset button.

13.2.3   Checking the results
After a program has been run the result may be stored somewhere in the memory. This location can be checked by once again using the 'M' command:

	Action	Comments
Response	*	Monitor command mode.
Key in	M 000F	This requests the result of a program run, which is in location 000F.
Response	000F FC	The content (FC) displayed.
Key in	reset or carriage return	
Response	*	Monitor command mode returns.

13.2.4   Making a cassette or paper tape of a program

If a magnetic tape interface or a paper tape punch is available, most monitors allow programs to be stored in those forms. It is necessary to inform the monitor of the beginning and end addresses of the program to be saved in this way. The code letter for producing this operation might be 'P'.

	Action	Comments
	*	Monitor command mode.
Key in P	0100 01FF	Results in the memory contents of all locations between 0100 and 01FF being output to the tape interface or paper tape punch.

13.2.5   Loading the memory from paper or magnetic tape

Programs stored on punched tape or cassette may be loaded direct into the memory using the monitor 'load' command, which might use the letter 'L'. No memory location information is likely to be needed since most 'punch' commands actually create the tape with the addresses of the origin of the data included. The load command reads the addresses from the tape and restores the data to its original locations in the memory.

	Action	Comments
	*	Monitor command mode.
Key in	L	Loads/the memory from paper or magnetic tape.

13.2.6   Setting breakpoints

Because programs run so quickly, it is often very difficult to find errors. One way is to break up the program into segments and check that each part runs satisfactorily before moving on to the next. Setting a breakpoint means specifying the address terminating a segment; if, for example, the program is held between 0100 and 01FF, a breakpoint could be set at 0120. When the program is executed, on reaching the opcode before 0120, the processor will halt after outputting to the display the contents of its CPU registers. The programmer may then examine the register contents to see if the intended action was taking place; if so, a new breakpoint could be set at, say, 0150 and the process repeated. Breakpoints are diagnostic aids used for debugging programs. They are typically set as follows.

	Action	Comments
	*	Monitor command mode.
Key in	B 0120	Sets a breakpoint at 0120.

13.3   The location of the monitor

Most microprocessor systems have the ability to address 65K memory locations (0000 to FFFF hex). To avoid confusion, the designer of a computer system will allocate blocks of the memory space for specific purposes. Figure 13.1 illustrates how the memory space might be utilised. Such a diagram is called a **memory map**.

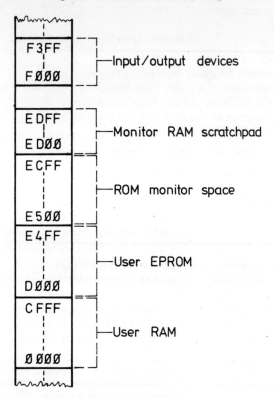

Fig. 13.1   A memory map

Input/output devices may use some locations and the ROM monitor program must be placed well outside the user RAM area. **User RAM** is the part of the memory into which the user writes his programs. Consequently the monitor is either pushed right to the top end of the memory, or it commences at 0000 hex. This latter scheme is disadvantageous in systems using processors with facilities for base page addressing (see p. 68). In addition, monitors generally require a scratchpad area in RAM. Typically monitors may consist of from 255 to about 4K bytes, depending on complexity. The most popular size is about 1K.

The space for user EPROM may be used to accommodate the complex programs that the user has committed to read only memory. A BASIC interpreter is often treated in this way to save having to load the interpreter into RAM from a backing store such as a tape cassette or floppy disk.

13.4   Machine code programming

In machine code programming, the programmer converts his ideas into machine code instructions, thus carrying out the translation required to allow meaningful communication between himself and the machine. Because encoding in binary is so tedious, microprocessor systems usually allow programs to be written using hexadecimal code. Even so, the achievement of reasonably complex objectives requires firstly a comprehensive knowledge of the processor instruction set, and secondly the expense of a good deal of time and effort. There are circumstances, however, where this is justified. This will be discussed later in more detail.

13.5 Assembly language and assemblers

An alternative to programming in machine code is to use assembly language. In this case a program called an **assembler** is run on the system. Under the control of the assembler, the mnemonic inputs from the user's own program are converted in memory to machine code form.

It is considered that machine code instructions in hex form are hard to remember, but mnemonics, by definition, are not. Of course, for a certain operation more information than the mnemonic is required by the assembler program. Many operations can be carried out in a variety of addressing modes, so that this must be specified too. In addition some opcodes refer to absolute addresses or data and, if needed, these must be supplied.

A good assembler will allow program statements to be labelled and will therefore be able to calculate relative jumps in hex, or 2's complement hex, merely by references to the labels involved. In short, assembly language removes some of the more tedious chores involved in machine code programming. However, it must be remembered that assembler programs are CPU specific and so must be purchased or written with this in mind.

13.6 Using an assembler

The use of an assembler is best demonstrated by example. When the program runs, statements may be input. A statement is a program line commanding an operation. A typical format for statements might be

        LABEL (if required): mnemonic opcode tag name

The colon acts as a label terminator. 'Tag' would specify the addressing mode and 'name' could be the name of an I/O port or the name of a routine labelled elsewhere in the program. In the case where tag refers to the immediate mode of address, name would be replaced by literal data. Consider a statement to load accumulator A with FF (hex). It is assumed that the code is written for use on the Motorola M6802 CPU, and therefore the mnemonics are those associated with the instruction set for that machine.

Label	Mnemonic	Tag	Name
No label	LDAA	@	FF
		(signifies immediate mode)	(data)

The next statement is required to load the X register with a hex number that is to be decremented as part of a delay loop. This line is labelled, because it may be referred to from elsewhere in the program.

Label	Mnemonic	Tag	Name
WAIT:	LDX	@	3FFF
		(signifies immediate mode)	(data)

Branching from anywhere in the program to the wait routine referred to in the last example is achieved by the following statement:

Label	Mnemonic	Tag	Name
No label	BRA	R	WAIT
		(signifies relative mode)	

Suppose that the addresses associated with a PIA have been named as follows.

Memory location	Name	Comments
801C	DRA	Data register A side.
801D	CRA	Control register A side.
801E	DRB	Data register B side.
801F	CRB	Control register B side.

Once these labels have been declared to the assembler it is possible to write an initialisation program for the PIA. Note that the assembler must also be informed of the address at which the assembled program is to begin. Assume that the address 0000 is to be used and that the tag 'E' refers to the extended addressing mode. For the 6802 assembler the program would be written as follows.

Program lines			Explanation
LDAA	@	FF	Load accumulator A immediate with FF hex.
STAA	E	DRB	Store accumulator A extended in the data register of the B side.
LDAA	@	85	Load accumulator A immediate with 85 hex.
STAA	E	CRB	Store accumulator A extended in the control register of the B side.
LDAA	@	C3	Load accumulator A with C3 (hex) immediate.
STAA	E	CRA	Store accumulator A in A side control register.
LDAA	@	2B	Load accumulator A with 2B (hex) immediate.
STAA	E	DRB	Store accumulator A in the data register of the B side.

As a result of these program lines the assembler would produce the following machine code program.

Memory location	Hex code
0000	86 FF
0002	B7 801E
0005	86 85
0007	B7 801F

(continued opposite)

Memory location	Hex code
000A	86 C3
000C	B7 801D
000F	86 2B
0011	B7 801E

This, however, does not illustrate the use of labelling. Consider now the example of a delay loop, after which a jump to a print character subroutine is used.

```
WAIT:   LDX   @   3FFF
LOOP:   DEX
        BNE   R   LOOP
        JMP   E   PRINT
```

This would be assembled as

```
0000   CE   3FFF   Load X immediate with 3FFF.
0003   09          Decrement X.
0004   26   FD     Branch back to 0003 if not 0.
0006   7E   0100   Jump to a routine at 0100 (print).
```

13.7 System software

A complement to the assembler program is the **disassembler,** whose action is the reverse of the assembler in that having been fed a machine code program it outputs the mnemonics for each operation. This makes it possible to work out the principles behind a complex program without spending a long time looking up in the instruction set the function of each opcode.

Each program statement in mnemonics will be translated into a single machine code instruction, and for this reason both machine code and assembly language work are defined as **low-level programming**.

High-level languages allow programs to be written in a form that uses mostly English language words. The translator program is clearly commensurately more elaborate than the assembler required in low-level programming because each high-level program line may translate into many machine code instructions, whereas in assembler the ratio is one-to-one.

A high-level language translator program is called a **compiler** if it converts the entire high-level program into machine code before the program is executed. If the translator converts each program line to machine code as it executes, line by line, it is called an **interpreter**.

The work of a compiler or an interpreter is not simply one of translation; it must also check the program statements for errors in syntax or semantics. A syntax error involves the grammatically incorrect arrangement of words in a program statement. Semantics concerns whether or not the statement means anything in the language.

The use of compilers is gradually declining because of the greater upsurge of interest in the conversational mode, otherwise known as **interactive** computing, which involves the use of interpreters.

The interpreter must be loaded from some form of non-volatile store into the system RAM before high-level programming can commence. In general, interpreters require many thousands of memory locations and therefore in small systems this can be restrictive on the space left for user programs.

13.8   BASIC

Consideration of the amount of memory required for interpreters has led to the predominance of a language called BASIC in microsystem usage. This is a powerful, all-purpose language which has the advantages that it is easy to learn and use, and yet an interpreter giving full floating point arithmetic and an extensive vocabulary takes up only about 8K bytes of memory. Compared with interpreters for languages such as ALGOL, COBOL, FORTRAN, CORAL or PASCAL, this is most economical.

BASIC is a language which uses an amalgam of English words and algebra. All languages have rules for grammar, and BASIC is no exception. However, its rules are relatively simple and compared to 'natural' languages like French, English or Latin the vocabulary is very limited. Programs in BASIC are written as a series of statements or lines. Each line is uniquely numbered at the beginning and consists of an **operator** or **keyword** and at least one **operand**. For example:

10	INPUT	X, Y, Z
line number	keyword	operands

The keyword defines the operation that is to be carried out. The operands are what are operated upon. Line number 10 commands the input of three numbers. The numbers are to be labelled consecutively X, Y and Z.

A BASIC program

The object of this program is to convert metres per second to miles per hour, and to print the result in miles per hour plus the equivalent number of kilometres per hour.

```
10   PRINT "HOW MANY METRES PER SECOND?"
20   INPUT A
30   IF A = 0 THEN 90
40   LET K = A * 3600/1000
50   LET M = K * 5/8
60   PRINT "KM/HR", "MILES/HR"
70   PRINT K, M
80   GO TO 20
90   END
```

The program explained

Line 10   The PRINT instruction or keyword tells the computer to output to the terminal (VDU or teletype) the characters between the inverted commas.

Line 20   INPUT tells the computer to expect a number input from the terminal, and that this number shall be labelled 'A'.

Line 30   The keywords IF and THEN allow a conditional jump to take place. If the number labelled A is equal to zero, program execution continues from line 90; otherwise the computer moves to the next highest numbered line.

Line 40   LET assigns a value to a variable labelled 'K'. In this case the number labelled A is multiplied by 3600 and divided by 1000 to produce the variable K.

Line 50   This assigns the label 'M' to a number calculated by multiplying K by 5 and dividing the result by 8.

Line 60   Outputs to the terminal the column headings for kilometres per hour and miles per hour.

Line 70   Outputs under the column headings the numbers labelled K and M.

Line 80   Is an unconditional command to continue the program from line 20; in other words, expect a new input value for A.

Line 9Ø   The keyword END signifies that program execution should cease. The program is finished. This line in the example program is only reached should the input value of A be zero.

A program like this actually comprises a very large number of machine code instructions, and obviously it is much easier for a user to be able to program in this way. Why, then, are not all programs written in high level languages? Firstly, microprocessor-based systems dedicated to a particular job will not have the necessary quantity of random access memory to accommodate the high-level language interpreter; and secondly, in machine control programs, efficiency is paramount. When a program is written in a high-level language it uses a number of standardised machine code routines within the interpreter. No short cuts are possible and so the program execution time will be longer than if a specific machine code program were written for the purpose. Another delay aspect is that concerned with checking line by line for errors in syntax and semantics, and translating English-type statements to machine code.

For applications like this, the extra time and effort of programming in machine code or assembler is necessary.

14
Magnetic disc systems

14.1   The reasons for dominance

The use of discs for the permanent storage of programs and data has a number of advantages. To appreciate this statement consider the other options. What about magnetic tape? Firstly, tape backing stores are sequential devices, that is to say, data is stored in records that are 'one after the other' on the tape. Consequently, to find a wanted piece of information the tape has to be searched, going through all the records that are not wanted until reaching the record that is wanted. Tape access is, therefore, relatively slow. What about magnetic bubble memory? These devices are still sequential stores but because they have no mechanical moving parts, access times are very fast, in fact, not much slower than main semiconductor memory. Unfortunately, the technology of bubble memory has been difficult to implement and has taken considerable develop-ment capital. This means that bubble memory costs to the end user are still high. Magnetic disc technology, on the other hand, offers fast access times because it is a form of random access store. The discs themselves are the same media as magnetic tape but use, by comparison, relatively little material. The discs, then, are cheap, and they give acceptable performance at reasonable cost.

Data is stored on the disc as a series of magnetic states. However, it is not possible simply to store 0s and 1s as magnetic domains with opposite magnetic polarity, because reading the data off the disc is based on picking up changes of field direction. Such changes would not be detected if a stored word contained a number of consecutive 0s or 1s. This problem is overcome by an ingenious technique, which will be explained in Section 14.3.2.

14.1.1   Types of disc
The idea of disc storage can be implemented in various ways depending on the specifica-tion and intended use of the computer working with the disc system. A low cost implementation of reasonable reliability for a computer that accesses the disc relatively infrequently and for which data transfer rates need not be the highest possible, is the **floppy disc** system.

A floppy disc is made of a thin and flexible base material which is coated with a ferro-magnetic surface. To make handling easier, and also to afford some protection, the disc is permanently housed in a stiff envelope. Access to the disc for reading and writing pur-poses is through an aperture cut in the envelope. This arrangement is shown in Fig. 14.1.

14.1.2   Floppy disc organisation
Given that a method of storing magnetic states is available, what are its characteristics? Data is resident on the disc in circular **tracks**. These tracks are individual and not spiral as in the case of gramophone records. There are usually between 35 and 80 such tracks on a disc, depending on the system being used. Each track is made up of **sectors**, with between 8 and 20 sectors in each. A sector is enough space to store 128 or 256 bytes. Clearly,

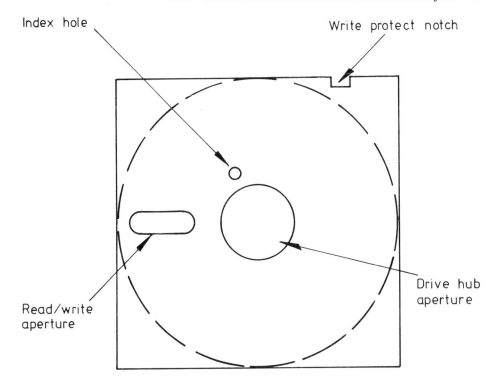

Index hole

Write protect notch

Drive hub aperture

Read/write aperture

Fig. 14.1 Floppy disc details

simple arithmetic shows that if a disc has 80 tracks with 20 sectors and 256 bytes in each sector, it may store $80 \times 20 \times 256 = 409\ 600$ bytes. In some systems both sides of the disc can be used giving a total of some 800K bytes of storage. The arrangement of tracks and sectors is shown in Fig. 14.2.

14.1.3 A disc system
Disc systems are a complex form of technology and to appreciate them fully the system should be considered as consisting of three sub-systems.

1) The disc drive mechanism and electrical interface.
2) The disc controller.
3) The disc operating system software.

Each of these subsystems will be looked at in detail.

14.2 Disc drive mechanism and electrical interface

The drive mechanism is housed in a chassis frame, with a door or a slot at one end. Located on the chassis there will be a printed circuit board carrying the interface circuits. There will also be a read/write head, and a mechanism for moving the head radially over the disc surface. A number of types of mechanism exist, of which one of the most popular uses a stepper motor driving a worm gear. As the motor turns, the head carriage will move in and out. The movement will be incremental.

The floppy disc itself, when in position, must be rotated at about 300 rpm. This is

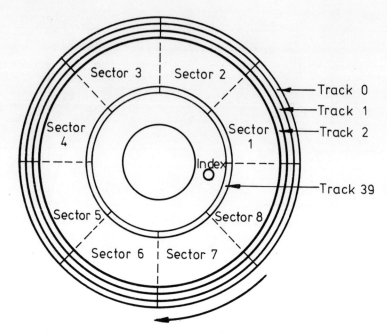

Fig. 14.2   Disc storage format

done by means of a clutch drive system interlocked with the disc drive door or loading switch. A DC motor, with servo feedback to maintain a constant speed, is connected to the clutch drive.

In floppy disc drives the read/write head actually contacts the surface of the disc during read/write activity. Clearly this situation would give rise to a lot of wear if the disc was rotated continuously. This is combatted by only rotating the disc when the computer wants to access data. Obviously the data might be stored in different radial positions on the disc and so, at times, the disc would be rotating when the radial position stepper motor has to move the head carriage. It would not be wise to keep the read/write head in contact with the surface during this movement and so a separate mechanism is provided to lift the head from the surface under these circumstances. This device is the **head load** mechanism. The general arrangement is shown in Fig. 14.3.

It should now be evident that, in order to work the drive successfully, the computer interface to the drive will have to:

1)   supply signals to switch on the disc rotational motor;
2)   supply other signals to control the head position stepper;
3)   supply the head load signal.

However, the picture is still more complex. Many more signals than these are needed. To understand the extra requirements it is necessary to grasp the basic layout of storage for data on the disc. It has already been explained that data is stored magnetically in a series of concentric tracks and sectors. Stepping the read/write head radially is the means of locating the tracks, but a method must also be provided to identify the start of a given track. Look at Fig. 14.1. Near to the centre hole, used by the clutch system to rotate the disc, is another much smaller hole. This is the index hole. On the disc itself is a hole punched through at exactly the radius corresponding to the index hole in the disc envelope. Consequently, as the disc is rotated, once per revolution the holes are aligned. Mounted within the drive chassis is a light source and matching detector, placed on either

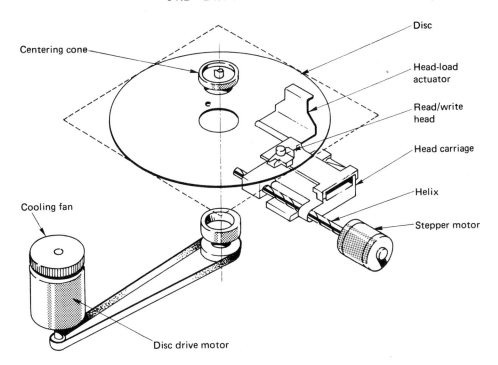

Fig. 14.3   Disc drive mechanism

side of the disc. The detector only 'sees' the source when the holes are aligned. This fact is used to generate a signal out of the disc drive, and the signal is used to identify the start of each track.

So far no consideration has yet been given to the read/write head or power supplies. Energising currents produced by the disc controller to store or erase the data must be passed across the interface. Disc drives normally require multiple power supplies to operate their various actuators and transducers. Typically +5 V and +12 V are required.

There are some further points concerning read/write head loading and movement. For example, the use of a stepper motor does allow the possibility of using an open loop system for locating the tracks on the disc surface. For the most part this is done, but there is a need for the disc controller to have some 'known' point of reference for it to avoid losing positional information. The known point of reference is usually the outermost track on the disc. This track is called track 0. Track 0 is located when the system is initialised at power-up. To be sure of finding it, the controller need only step the head carriage out to the limit by producing a continuous train of pulses and then monitor the state of a feedback line driven by a microswitch which signals when track 0 is reached. Once the seek track 0 command is fulfilled, the controller then tells the stepper motor driving the head carriage to reverse direction, and it then pulses the motor the requisite number of times to put the read/write head over the required track.

It must be appreciated that the disc drive mechanism is a relatively unintelligent device and therefore it should be no surprise that it has to be told, by the disc controller, what to do in a step-by-step sequence to achieve even the simplest action (see Fig. 14.4). Consider the number of controlled and monitored elements within the drive. There is the disc rotating motor that must be switched on when an access is imminent. The drive will probably signal when the disc is rotating at the correct speed by asserting the ready feedback line to the controller. When this is done the controller must achieve **datum** position for

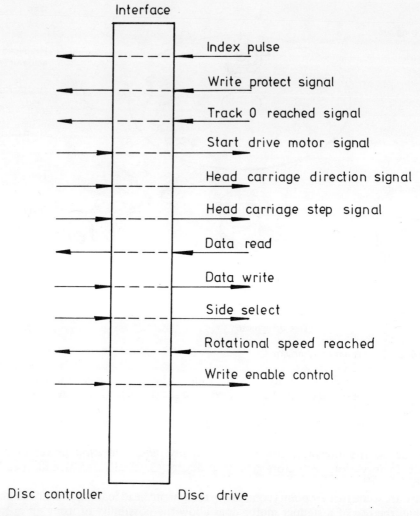

Fig. 14.4   Disc drive control signals

the read/write head, that is, the controller must command seek track 0. This may well entail the controller producing a two state **direction** signal with the correct polarity, and then providing a series of pulses to the head carriage stepper motor until the track 0 feedback line is active. The controller will now need to reverse the polarity of the direction line and generate pulses to the stepper to locate the required track. This done, the read/write head will be **loaded,** that is it will be brought into contact with the disc surface, usually by a solenoid type device. Actuation of the solenoid requires a signal from the controller. The controller must now monitor the state of the **index** transducer line looking for the start of the track. When the track is found the controller must use the read/write head to read sector information until the correct sector identity is detected. Over and above all this the disc controller must not attempt to write a sector if the **write protection** slot is covered. This is determined by a sensor in the drive signalling over yet another wire.

The impression gained by this last review is that a large number of separate signals have to pass between the controller and the drive and that the drive itself is essentially a 'dumb' peripheral. This is basically true and it can be expected that the electrical interface to the drive could comprise a connector carrying about 17 signal conductors.

14.3   Disc controller

The source of the signals required to operate the disc drive has been referred to as the **controller**. The controller can take various forms but just two examples will be considered:

1) the 'soft' controller;
2) the dedicated hardware controller.

However, before the action of these controllers can be considered, it is necessary to understand at two levels how data is encoded on the disc. The first requirement is a complete grasp of what constitutes a sector, and then the exact way in which data is recorded on a disc must be understood.

14.3.1   Track and sector format
The most flexible way of establishing sectors or formatting a track on a disc is by software. This is referred to as **soft sectoring**. With a soft sectored system the formatting process must be applied to the disc before use and produces a framework or skeleton for sectors into which data can be written. A format for a complete track is shown in Fig. 14.5 where there are 20 sectors. As mentioned earlier, the index output of the drive consists of a pulse occurring once per revolution of the disc when the index hole is optically sensed. The leading edge of this pulse marks the beginning of the track which is identified by the **index address mark**.

Index

Gap	Index Address Mark	Gap	Sector 1	Sector 2		Sector 19	Sector 20	Gap	Gap	Index Address Mark

Fig. 14.5   Details of track recording format

The detailed form of the framework is of the kind shown in Fig. 14.6.

Gap	Identity Address Mark	Track Address	Zero	Sector Address	CRC	Identity Address Mark	Data	CRC	Gap

Identify field   Data field

Fig. 14.6   Details of a single sector

Each sector is made up of two fields or parts. The **identity** or ID field and the **data** field. The ID field contains the binary numbers describing the track and sector address. Preceding the track address sub-field there is the **identity address mark** or ID AM sub-field. The purpose of ID AM is to tell the controller that there is an address coming up and to warn it to be ready. The controller uses the zero sub-field to differentiate between

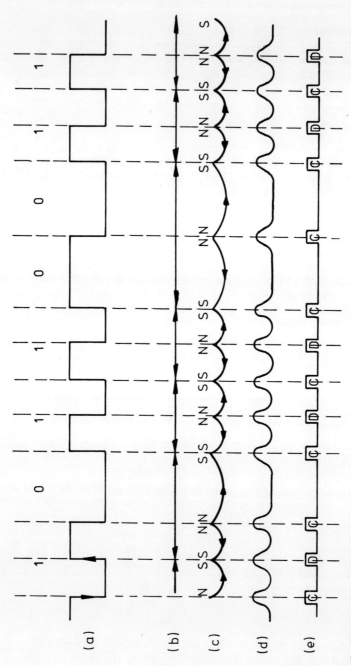

Fig. 14.7   FM recording techniques

track number and sector number information. The zero field is a long string of binary zeros. At the end of the ID field there is the CRC sub-field. CRC stands for cyclic redundancy check and is a form of error detection scheme.

The format of the data field can be seen to be similar, with a preceding address mark and trailing CRC checks surrounding the information of interest. In this case the information of interest is the save program or data code. The purpose of the format can be seen to be to allow the disc controller to separate the vital pieces of information it needs, and also to have the ability to **verify** that no data corruption has taken place. The data field itself may have its length determined by instructions from the disc control programs in the computer system. Typical commercial systems usually produce 128, 256, 512 or even 1024 byte data fields for each sector.

14.3.2   Data recording methods

As mentioned earlier, it is necessary to have a general understanding of how individual 0s and 1s are transferred on and off the disc. There are a number of encoding and decoding standards of which the following will serve as an example and is the method used most often to produce single density recording. The technical name for this method is **Biphase-Mark**, but it is very often referred to as FM. Figure 14.7 shows a time related set of waveforms and magnetic domain information.

The read/write head of the disc drive is a ferrite core with an air gap and a coil wound on the core. When a current passes through the coil the resulting magnetic field follows the path of least reluctance. It is therefore mainly confined to the core, but must bridge the air gap to complete the magnetic circuit. At the gap, **fringing** of the field occurs so that the field cuts the ferrite disc material that is adjacent. Figure 14.8 illustrates these principles.

Referring to the time related waveforms and magnetic domains shown in Fig. 14.7 waveform (a) is the current required in the read/write head to record the byte 10110011. The principle of bi-phase mark recording is that each recorded bit takes a specific time to be written or read. Consequently, the inference is that each bit has a specific length on the disc because the disc rotates under the head at a constant speed. Each bit period starts with a current reversal. If a '1' is to be recorded, a second transition takes place in the middle of the allowed bit time.

If a 0 is to be recorded, no second reversal takes place. The appearance of waveform (a) explains why this method has come to be called FM. The waveform resembles a square wave that is frequency modulated. However, the current directions are responsible for magnetising the disc surface as shown in (b). Once the surface has been

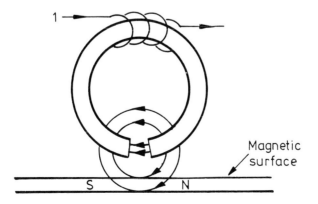

Fig. 14.8   Read/write head

magnetised in this way a track is analogous to a lot of small magnets placed end to end. The remanent flux will produce a field series as shown in (c). When a conductor moves with respect to a field a voltage will be induced into the conductor. During a read event, the disc rotates under the head inducing a voltage into it proportional to the rate of change of flux. Waveform (d) shows the result in this case. After processing and shaping, a rectangular wave train as in (e) is produced. Note that the pulses due to the beginning of each bit period are denoted C. This stands for 'clock' since they are regular and used for timing purposes by the disc controller. When the controller is to read a byte, it synchronises to the bit rate by examining these clock pulses. It is then required to sample after half a bit period to detect the presence of a pulse. If a pulse is detected then a 1 is read; if no pulse is present a 0 is read.

14.3.3　Soft controllers
In the case of a **soft controller** the 17 or so conductors needed to operate the drive are connected to the peripheral side of a parallel port such as a PIO or PIA (see Chapter 10). The port would be configured for individual bit control, and would be addressable over the bus system. The hardware is therefore very simple but the responsibility for causing each action of the disc drive is that of the operating system software. To start the rotational motor, to step the head carriage, or to load the read/write head will all require a write cycle of the system's central processor. The operating system software must therefore contain routines to change individual bit states at the output of a parallel port. To produce a useful disc drive action requires a sequence of bit state changes, and so it can be readily appreciated that the operating system software will be quite involved and will use up a lot of the central processor's time. If the central processor is having to generate every tiny step in controlling the drive, it cannot be doing anything else. It is for this reason that the soft controller method is in general held to be inefficient. It does, however, have one advantage. It is cheap to implement. Consequently it has been used in a number of popular microcomputer systems, where a large work throughput is not expected. The system is shown in Fig. 14.9.

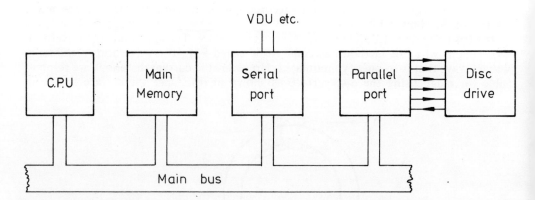

Fig. 14.9　Soft controller disc drive interface arrangement

14.3.4　The dedicated hardware controller
The object of introducing a **dedicated** hardware controller is to improve the performance by comparison with the soft controller system. The idea is to devolve the lower level control functions to an interface circuit that is more intelligent than a simple parallel port. The minimum requirement is that the dedicated controller be able to **sequence** the transitions of the lines to the disc drive. What sequence is generated must be dependent

upon an **instruction word** sent by the system's main central processor. In this way a sequence of many bit state changes can be initiated by one write cycle of the system processor. The instruction words are often referred to as **macros**. The complexity of an LSI (large scale integrated) disc controller can be as involved as that of a single chip microcomputer and the principles are best described by the example shown in Fig. 14.10.

A dedicated LSI controller IC must be able to generate the detailed sequences required by the drive from a simple command set. Also, the semiconductor manufacturer who makes it must allow for system designers to choose certain options about how it will operate. The choices will be dependent on the hardware specification of the disc drive units chosen for the computer. For example, some drives require a three phase drive signal for their stepper motors, others need simple step and direction signals. Different drives have different track to track stepping times and different times for the head load action to 'settle', before data transfers should take place. In addition, the system designer should be given the freedom to determine how many bytes will be stored in each sector. The manufacturer has an incentive to make his product appeal to as many system designers as possible and so it is usual to have 'programmable' disc controller ICs. This will mean that the device will have to be **initialised**, that is, control words must be sent to it on power up to tailor it's operation to the system in which it is used.

The bus interface

The requirement to initialise, to receive commands, and to send and receive data to and from the host system gives a clue to the connections needed between the dedicated disc controller IC and the host computer's bus system. The bus interface must allow the device to appear as a number of addressable registers. This can be achieved by each register being allocated a port address or by a memory mapped arrangement. It depends upon whether the system CPU has special input/output arrangements or not.

One popular device provides two lines expected to be connected to the lowest order address lines A0 and A1. For unique address mapping all the other address bus lines would be applied to combinational logic to derive a 'chip select' signal active only when a specific block of four addresses appeared on the address bus. At first sight this would seem to give access to only four registers. In fact five registers can be reached. The reason for this is that of the five internal registers two do not require to have both read and write access. They can therefore share an address — which one is dealt with can be arbitrated by the state of the read/write control line from the processor. This kind of technique is common in LSI bus interfacing. The name and purpose of each of the five programmable internal registers in the example controller are now described.

The command register

The controller expects to receive commands generated by the disc operating system (DOS) software. This is a one way traffic situation, and so from the point of view of the computer bus this register is write only.

The status register

This register is a group of flags, the purpose of which is to indicate the current state of the device. The meaning assigned to the flags often depends upon the command currently being dealt with by the controller. For simple commands such as seek a particular track, or step the head carriage in or out, the individual bits of the status register carry feedback information such as head loaded, track 0 found, disc is write protected and the like. Obviously the DOS software ought not to command write sector unless the head is loaded. It should also issue an error message such as cannot write to disc if the write protection slot of the disc itself is covered. The only way that the DOS can find out this kind of information is by reading the status register of the disc controller IC. The register

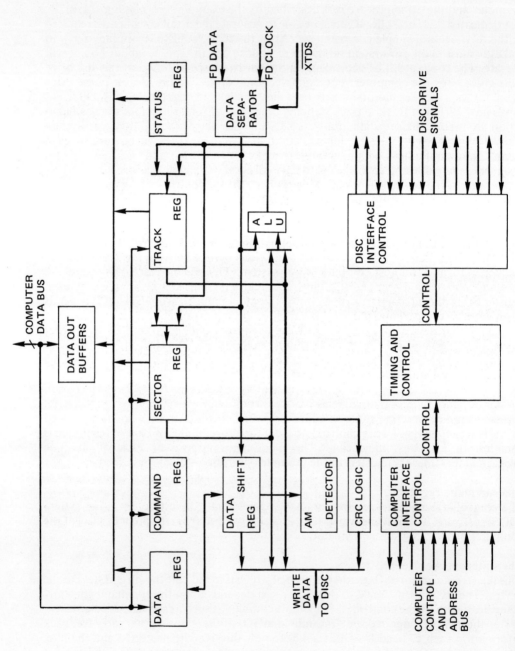

Fig. 14.10 Disc controller IC (courtesy of Western Digital Corporation)

has its bits set and cleared from the disc drive electronics, and thus from the computer bus side, only read actions are required.

Track and sector registers

Each sector carries identification of its position on the disc in terms of its track and sector. In accessing a disc file the DOS first consults the disc directory to discover the **disc addresses** involved. When the head carriage is **stepped** in or out the track register is incremented or decremented appropriately so that it always contains the number of the track directly under the read/write head. When a 'read sector' operation is being carried out the DOS will know the track of the target sector and produces **step pulses** checking the current track position of the head by reading the track register until it is the same as the required track number. When the correct track has been located it is usual to read the identification of track inherent to each sector to verify that the head position is truly as expected. This function allows the DOS to ensure that nothing is amiss and that the drive is behaving properly.

The sector register is loaded by the DOS with the desired sector number. Assuming that the correct track has been found, the sector identification is read off each sector as it passes under the head. This is then compared with the contents of the sector register until the correct sector is found. The data in the sector will now be transferred to or from the disc. In order to control the correct head carriage motion to find a given sector from an arbitrary position the DOS will have to read the current head position which will always be in the track register.

Data registers

Data words for storage are passed over the computer bus as parallel words. This conflicts with the nature of the disc storage read and write actions because each bit of the data word is recorded as magnetic states in a sequential manner. This is a serial method within the context of a sector. There is therefore a need for parallel-to-serial data conversion. A straightforward parallel in, parallel out register interfaces to the bus and content is transferred to a shift register for reading or writing to the disc. This shift register has to be bi-directional, i.e. parallel in, serial out for writing, and serial in, parallel out for reading.

Data separator

The waveform of Fig. 14.7 (e) shows that clock and data pulses are interspersed as the head reads the disc. The question arises as to how the controller separates the two. The means of separation is inherent in the address mark fields of each sector. Certain clock pulses are missed during the recording process. A certain pattern is decided upon for the data words within the address mark field. The combination of missing clocks and the pattern of 0s and 1s in the data pattern lead to a unique set of circumstances which enable the controller to determine which of the pulses are clocks and which are data. Once this is determined it becomes possible to phase lock an internal voltage controlled oscillator to the clock frequency coming off the disc and so generate the correct sampling **window** when valid data pulses are present.

The ALU

During the description of the track and sector registers it became evident that comparisons would need to be made between the desired track or sector and those currently passing under the read head. Since the data can now be separated from the clocks the content of the track address field or the sector address field can be compared with the appropriate register. Comparison can be achieved by subtraction. If the result is zero the target has been found. This fact can be used to switch the controller's activity from searching to reading the data field of the sector.

14.4   Disc operating system software

Information is stored on disc in formal structures called data files. The addition of a disc drive to a system allows the recall of a large amount of data from any of these files, but at the same time gives rise to the need for the user to control many more data processing options. Clearly, maintaining the existence of data files, the addition of new material to old files, the creation of completely new files and the deletion of old material will be the kind of things a user will want to do. Regular requirements like this could be achieved, for example, by the user writing the necessary routines to operate the disc drive to retrieve a data file. However, as must be obvious from previous work on the disc drive mechanism and disc controller circuits, it would mean that such users would have to be very expert and also very familiar with their own hardware.

Most people using computers are not going to be able to do this, and in any case it does not make sense for the same work to be achieved over and over again. Software vendors have seen this opportunity and suitable **control** programs can be readily purchased. Although individual control programs will do jobs such as format a new disc, create a new file, rename files, delete files and so on, the obvious thing to do is market a collection of them as a package. Packages of control programs are called **operating systems**, and operating systems that are largely biassed towards disc storage functions are called **disc operating systems**.

14.4.1   DOS organisation

An operating system can be broken down so that its control programs fall into three main categories. The three categories are illustrated in Fig. 14.11.

The file manager software contains all the control programs for handling data storage on the disc, while the resource manager allocates the resources available to the system. In a multi-user system it is the resource manager that finds individual users working space in memory and connects I/O handlers appropriately. I/O handlers or drivers are programs that organise the proper working of particular peripherals, such as VDUs, serial printer ports, parallel printer ports, and so on. It should be appreciated that different routines may be required for each case. In a single user system the resource manager will be much simpler than its counterpart is in a computer system handling multi-user activity.

The executive is a collection of programs which knit the whole thing together and

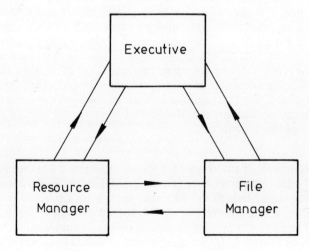

Fig. 14.11   Elements of a DOS

present an 'intelligent face' to the user. One of the programs within the executive is the keyboard command interpreter. This program automatically runs when nothing else is going on. Its purpose is to collect commands from the system master keyboard when such commands arise. It is through the keyboard command interpreter that all other DOS functions are reached.

14.4.2   DOS residence
Now that it has been established that the DOS is software, the question arises as to where this software resides. In a few exceptional cases the DOS may be held in read only memory (ROM). Most serious users find this arrangement insufficiently flexible because there is no reason why those with enough knowledge and skill should not be able to add extra control programs of their own devising, or even modify the existing DOS package. ROM based DOS would clearly make this difficult.

The alternative, which is universally popular, has the DOS software on disc. A computer using this method would have nearly all the memory space implemented in RAM. Nearly all, because the requirements for loading the DOS into the RAM from the disc will demand a very small loader program to be permanently available as firmware in ROM.

14.4.3   DOS bootstrapping
The nature of the action of the loader program is worthy of consideration. Normally, loading is achieved using a primary and secondary process. The primary loader is the ROM resident program referred to previously. A few tens of machine code instructions address the disc controller, resetting it before issuing the seek track zero command. After a suitable delay, when the disc drive is at the correct speed and track zero found, the primary loader reads the first few sectors. These sectors contain the secondary loader. Once the secondary loader is installed in an arbitrary area of memory, the primary loader has done its job and its last instruction is to jump unconditionally to the start of the secondary loader. The secondary loader, being a more elaborate program, pulls the majority part of the operating system off of the disc and puts it into main memory, usually near the top of the memory map. Having done this it transfers control to the executive of the DOS which performs some initialising operations before executing the keyboard command interpreter. This complete action is called **bootstrapping** the DOS into existence.

14.4.4   The transitory program area
The size of the operating system put into main memory by the loader would not normally exceed about 16K. This would leave the lower 48K of main memory free. This area is called the transitory program area (TPA), and the DOS will put the user's choice of programs in it. What is meant by the user's choice? Perhaps a high level language interpreter or a text editor is required. The system model so far described would have these programs stored on disc, and simply calling for one of them would cause the DOS to fetch it into the TPA. The DOS would then automatically run the program.

Imagine that a user wished to write a BASIC program. Assuming that the DOS keyboard interpreter is ready, the BASIC interpreter has first to be loaded, perhaps into the lowest part of the TPA. When this has been done and the BASIC interpreter is running the user may now commence writing in BASIC. The program he writes will be to solve a particular problem for which it has been decided to use the computer. As such, his program will be an **application** program. The text for the application program will be kept in the TPA, above the interpreter program. The interpreter program, because it enables applications to be generated on the system, is called a **system** program.

It can now be seen that the TPA can be occupied by system or applications programs or both. Either are users' choice options. The important point is that a user can finish with one system or application program and then, provided he can get back to the DOS keyboard command interpreter, he can call a different option into the TPA. The DOS is permanently resident in the top part of the memory, whereas the TPA holds transitory users' options.

14.4.5   Further aspects of DOS residence

It has been stated that the DOS is permanently resident. This statement needs qualifying because it implies that all the features of a complex set of control programs can be fitted into 16K. This is absurd, so what is the truth of the matter? In reality the 16K is filled with control programs which are used either continuously or frequently. The less heavily used options are not included. If they are needed they are fetched from the disc and executed whilst in the TPA, just as if they were the system programs spoken of earlier. Conceptually, the DOS may be viewed as consisting of resident or non-resident parts, the latter being those programs executed in the TPA. Some components of the DOS are necessarily of the resident variety. These include the keyboard command interpreter, the fundamental file management programs, and the fundamental input/output driver routines. It is up to the DOS software designer to decide which features of the DOS are fundamental. To arrive at an example it will be necessary to list typical DOS control routines.

Table 14.1 lists with comments a typical collection of control programs which might make up a commercial DOS package.

Table 14.1   Typical DOS routines

Program name	Purpose
DIRectory	Used to obtain a list of system or application programs on a disc
ERAse	Used to erase or delete a disc file
REName	Used to change the name of a disc file
SAVE	Create a new disc file
TYPE	Show the content of the file on the VDU
COPY	Copy files from one peripheral to another i.e. from disc drive A to drive B
SPOOL	Send a file to the queue of files for printing
FORMAT	Initialise a new floppy disc with the skeleton of tracks and sectors

These programs would be supplemented by a range of others which fall into two categories. Firstly, there are the more sophisticated control types. One example of this might be when a DOS is required to store newly created machine code programs in hex-ASCII form. This is done to allow easier documenting, but the problem is that the code is not executable. In order to be able to run the program it has to be changed from hex-ASCII to binary form. One major operating system has this program. It is called **LOAD**. As another example, some DOS allow the details of communication within the I/O system to be changed, i.e. there may be a need for flexible setting of the various control characters such as backspace, the delete character, or the end of line character. It may also be an advantage to be able to set the page length or width for text, or switch on an end of page pause feature. One DOS which has this capability calls the program that controls it **TTYSET**. In practice there are likely to be a number of programs of this kind.

The second category of supplementary programs would include text editors, debuggers, high level languages. The chances are that the listed programs such as DIRectory, ERAse, and so on would be permanently resident, as would some of the more sophisticated control programs. Other sophisticated or less used options would be non-resident, that is they would be called into the TPA as required. Text editors, debuggers, and high level languages would all be non-resident.

What has been covered so far is about the limit to which generalisation can be applied. Different DOS packages have different sources and although likenesses to the basic principles can always be identified, variations abound. Individual DOS documentation must be studied carefully. The aim of this section has been to introduce the fundamentals so that the DOS documentation can begin to be comprehensible.

15
Practical exercises

It must be appreciated that the exercises which follow are designed to be general in their application. For this reason, the addresses used in example programs may have to be changed if the system used does not have suitably placed random access memory.

In the same way, references to monitor addresses or routines have been made non-specific. The relevant documentation on individual monitor programs must be consulted, and appropriate addresses inserted. Where addresses must be inserted, asterisks (*) are present in the programs.

The experiments are concerned only with machine code instructions for the 6802, 8085 and 6502 processors, but the use of the flow diagrams together with an instruction set should allow programs achieving the objectives to be written for any processor. It has been previously pointed out that programs written in 8085 code will run on a Z80 system, but it should be noted that the mnemonic codes used are those associated with the 8085, which differ from the Z80 set. The hexadecimal codes are, however, identical.

15.1 Exercises for the 6802

Exercise 1

1.1 Object
To load and run a program using immediate and direct addressing that adds two hexadecimal numbers together.

1.2 Flow diagram

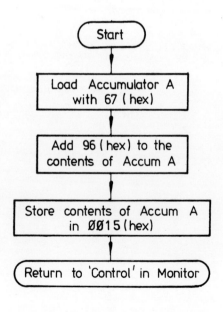

Fig. 15.1

1.3   Machine code program

Memory location	Machine code	Mnemonic	Comments
0000	86	LDAA	Load (immediate) accumulator A
0001	67	data	with 67 (hex).
0002	8B	ADDA	Add immediate
0003	96	data	96 (hex) to accumulator A contents.
0004	97	STAA	Store (direct) the contents
0005	15	address	of accumulator A in address (00)15.
0006	7E	JMP	Return control to
0007	* ⎫	monitor	monitor.
0008	* ⎭	address	

After executing the program correctly, memory location 0015 should hold the result of adding 96 (hex) to 67 (hex).

1.4   Loading the program
Load the program using the appropriate monitor commands. Before running the program, load memory location 0015 with 00 (hex) so that the correct execution of the program can be checked.

1.5   Running and checking correct program execution
Run the program and check its correct execution by examining the contents of memory location 0015, e.g.

$$67 \text{ in binary form} = 01100111$$
$$96 \text{ in binary form} = \underline{10010110}$$
$$67 + 96 \text{ in binary form} = \underline{11111101}$$
$$11111101 \text{ in hexadecimal form} = FD$$

If the program has been correctly executed the contents of location 0015 should be FD.

1.6   Task
Write, load, and then test the machine code program for the flow diagram shown in Fig. 15.2 overleaf. The starting address in RAM for the program is to be 0060 (hex).

Exercise 2

2.1   Object
To load and run a program which:

a)   adds two numbers together using direct addressing throughout;
b)   adds two numbers together using extended addressing throughout.

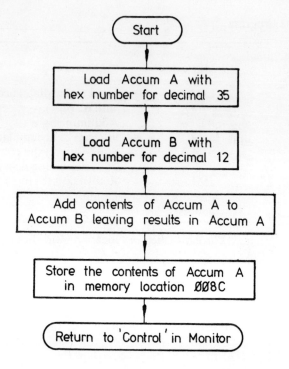

Fig. 15.2

2.2 Flow diagram

(a) Direct Addressing   (b) Extended Addressing

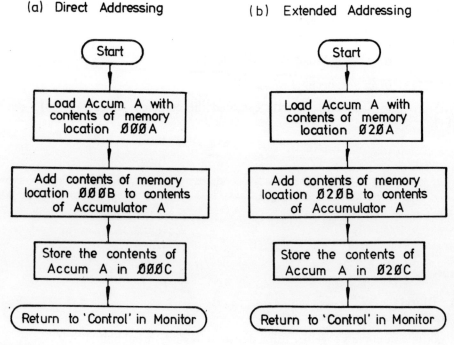

Fig. 15.3

2.3   Machine code program using direct addressing

Memory location	Hex code	Mnemonic	Comments
0000	96	LDAA	Load (direct) accumulator A with
0001	0A	address	contents of memory location (00)0A.
0002	9B	ADDA	Add (direct) contents of memory
0003	0B	address	location (00)0B to contents of accumulator.
0004	97	STAA	Store (direct) accumulator
0005	0C	address	contents in memory location (00)0C.
0006	7E	JMP	Return to control in
0007	*	monitor	monitor.
0008	*	address	
000A	67	data	First number (addend).
000B	96	data	Second number (augend).
000C			Result (sum).

The first instruction LDAA causes the data held in memory location 000A, i.e. 67 (hex), to be loaded into the accumulator. Because the number is held within the first 256 bytes of memory, direct addressing can be used, with only the least significant 8 bits being used to identify the memory location.

The second and third instructions, using direct addressing, cause the contents of memory location 000B, i.e. 96 (hex), to be added to the contents of accumulator A with the result being stored in 000C.

2.4   Procedure for program operation
a)   Load and then run the program.
b)   Check the correct execution of the program by going to memory location 000C and examining its contents; these should be FD.

2.5   Machine code program using extended addressing

Memory location	Hex code	Mnemonic	Comments
0000	B6	LDAA	Load (extended) accumulator A
0001	02	address	with contents of memory location
0002	0A		020A.
0003	BB	ADDA	Add (extended) to contents of accumulator A
0004	02	address	contents of memory location
0005	0B		020B.
0006	B7	STAA	Store (extended) contents of accumulator A
0007	02	address	in memory location 020C.
0008	0C		
0009	7E	JMP	Return to control in
000A	*	monitor	monitor.
000B	*	address	
020A	2A	data	First number (addend).
020B	46	data	Second number (augend).
020C			Result (sum).

The first instruction causes the data held in memory location 020A (hex 2A) to be loaded into accumulator A. As this memory location is outside the first 256 bytes of user RAM a two-byte memory address must be used. This is referred to as extended addressing and a different opcode is used.

The rest of the program is identical to the previous program except for the use of extended addressing.

2.6   Procedure for program operation
1)   Load and then run the program.
2)   Check the correct execution of the program by going to memory location 020C and examining its contents.

$$2A \text{ (hex)} = 00101010 \ +$$
$$46 \text{ (hex)} = 01000110$$
$$\overline{\phantom{46 \text{ (hex)} = }01110000}$$

Binary $01110000 = 70$ (hex)

The memory location 020C should contain 70 (hex).

2.7   Task
Write a program for the flow diagram in Fig. 15.4, using direct and extended addressing as appropriate. Place 35 (hex) in 013A and 59 (hex) in 0042.

Run the program and check its correct operation by examining the memory location where the result of the subtract operation is stored.

2.8 . Flow diagram

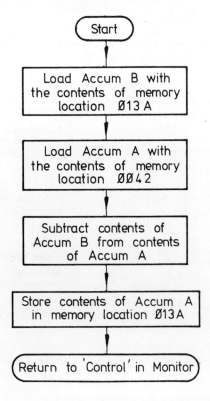

Fig. 15.4

Exercise 3

3.1   Object
To add two hexadecimal numbers together using the indexed mode of addressing:

(i)   without offset;   (ii)   with offset.

3.2   Flow diagram

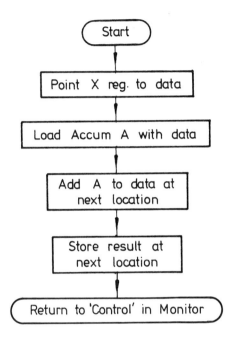

Fig. 15.5

3.3   Procedure without offset

Memory location	Hex code	Mnemonic	Comments
0100	CE	LDX	Load index register (immediate)
0101	02	data	with 0200.
0102	00		
0103	A6	LDAA	Load accumulator A with contents of the memory address
0104	00	data	pointed to by the X register.
0105	08	INX	Increase contents of index register by 1.
0106	AB	ADDA	Add to accumulator A contents of memory location pointed
0107	00	data	to by index register.
0108	08	INX	Increase contents of index register by 1.
0109	A7	STAA	Store A at the address
010A	00	data	pointed to by the index register.

(continued overleaf)

Memory location	Hex code	Mnemonic	Comments
010B	7E	JMP	Return control to
010C	* }	monitor	monitor.
010D	*	address	
0200	67	data	First number (addend).
0201	96	data	Second number (augend).
0202	00		Result (sum).

3.4   Procedure for program operation
Run the program and examine the contents of 0202.

3.5   Procedure with offset

Memory location	Hex code	Mnemonic	Comments
0100	CE	LDX　.	Load the index register with
0101	02 }	data	0200.
0102	00		
0103	A6	LDAA, X	Load accumulator A from the
0104	00	data	address pointed to by the index register.
0105	AB	ADDA, X	Add to accumulator A the contents of the location pointed
0106	01	data	to by the index register +1.
0107	A7	STAA, X	Store accumulator A contents in
0108	02	data	the address pointed to by the index register +2.
0109	7E	JMP	Return to control in
010A	* }	monitor	monitor.
010B	*	address	

3.6   Procedure for program operation
Run the program and examine the contents of 0202.

3.7   Task
Write a program to add three numbers together, taking care to ensure that the result does not exceed FF(hex)-255 decimal. The starting location of the program is to be 01DA, and that of the data 0000.

Exercise 4

4.1   Object
To write a simple program that uses jump and conditional branch instructions.

4.2   Program outline
The program is a software means of providing a variable time delay. When the program is run the processor will execute a loop for a set number of times before breaking out and returning to control in the monitor. The number of times the loop is executed can be

altered by changing two numbers, X and Y. The program starts at location 0100, with 0000 to 000F being available as a general scratchpad. It is in this scratchpad area at 0000 and 0001 that X and Y will be held.

4.3   Flow diagram

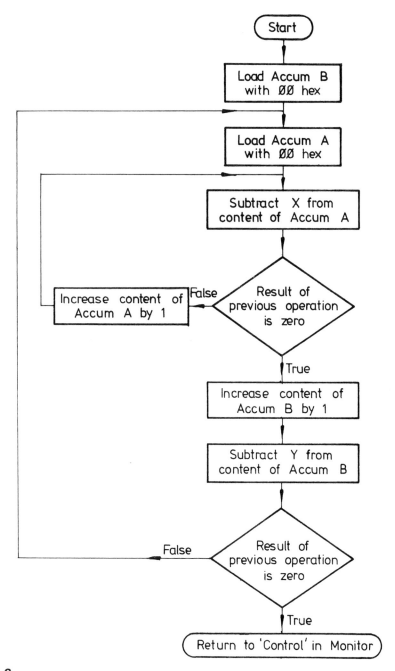

Fig. 15.6

4.4   Instructions used

Apart from the standard instructions, a number of more specialised instructions are used in the program. These are as follows.

CMPA   Compares the contents of accumulator A and the contents of a specified memory location. Result determines the state of certain condition flags.

CMPB   Compares the contents of the accumulator B and the contents of a specified memory location. Result determines the state of certain condition flags.

BEQ   Tests the state of the Z (zero) condition flag and causes a branch if the Z flag is set.

BRA   Program branches always to a point determined by the current value of the program counter plus the offset number stored in byte 2 of the instruction.

JMP   The program jumps to an address determined by byte 2 of the instruction.

4.5   Machine code program

Memory location	Hex code	Mnemonic	Comments
0000	FF	data	Terminating value for first loop — X.
0001	FF	data	Terminating value for second loop — Y.
0100	C6	LDAB	Load immediate accumulator B
0101	00	data	with 00 (hex).
0102	86	LDAA	Load immediate accumulator A
0103	00	data	with 00 (hex).
0104	91	CMPA	Subtract contents of memory location (00)00 (X) from
0105	00	data	contents of accumulator A.
0106	27	BEQ	Branch forward three locations if
0107	03	data	result of previous operation is zero, i.e. if Z flag set.
0108	4C	INCA	Increment contents of accumulator A by 1.
0109	20	BRA	Branch always back
010A	F9	data	seven locations from 010B to 0104.
010B	5C	INCB	Increment contents of accumulator B by 1.
010C	D1	CMPB	Subtract contents of memory location (00)01 (Y) from
010D	01	data	contents of accumulator B.
010E	27	BEQ	Branch forward three locations if
010F	03	data	result of previous operation is zero, i.e. if Z flag set.
0110	7E	JMP	Jump unconditionally to 0102.
0111	01 ⎫	address	
0112	02 ⎬		
0113	7E	JMP	Return to control in
0114	* ⎫	monitor	monitor.
0115	* ⎬	address	

When the program is run, starting at location 0100, the first two instructions LDAA and LDAB are concerned with setting the contents of both accumulators to zero.

The next instruction CMPA causes the contents of memory location 0000 (in the example, FF hex) to be subtracted from the contents of accumulator A. The result of executing this instruction will affect the status of some of the flags in the condition codes register. Only when the contents of the accumulator is equal to FF (hex) will the Z condition flag be set. Execution of CMPA does not cause the contents of accumulator A or memory location 0000 to be altered.

Memory location 0106 contains a conditional branch instruction — BEQ. The action of this instruction will depend upon the state of the Z flag. If the previous operation (CMPA) has resulted in the Z flag being set, the contents of the program counter will change by the number contained in byte 2 of the BEQ instruction. Remember that the program counter is already pointing to the next instruction, i.e. location 0108. Therefore, if the program counter is required to move forward to 010B it will only need to advance a further three memory locations. Thus, the offset in byte 2 of the BEQ instruction is +3 expressed as a 2's complement binary number, i.e.

$$+3 = 00000011 = 03 \text{ (hex)}$$

If the Z flag is not set the processor will just carry on executing instructions consecutively.

The BRA instruction held in location 0109 and 010A is a branch always instruction which when executed will cause the program counter to move the number of places indicated in byte 2 of the instruction. In the case of the example program, it is required that the program counter move backwards seven locations from 010B to 0104. Thus, the offset in byte 2 of the BRA instruction is −7 expressed as a 2's complement binary number, i.e.

$$+7 = 00000111$$
$$-7 = 11111000 + 1$$
$$= 11111001 = F9 \text{ (hex)}$$

An unconditional jump instruction is contained in locations 0110, 0111 and 0112. Bytes 2 and 3 of the JMP instruction contain the address to which the program counter has to jump.

4.6 Procedure for program operation
1) Load the program using FF (hex) for both X and Y. This will produce the maximum time delay.
2) Run the program starting at location 0100. Note the time lapse between running the program and the return to monitor prompt appearing on the display.
3) Change the numbers X and Y and note the different time delays obtained.

4.7 Task
A third 'delay' loop is to be added to increase the maximum time delay possible. As both A and B accumulators have been used in the previous loops some other way must be found for keeping track of the number of times the third loop is entered. One method is to use a selected memory location, say 0002 (hex), to hold initially the number of times that the third loop is to be entered. This number will be loaded in before the program is run. Each time the third loop is entered the contents of 0002 is decreased by one and the new number put back into 0002, i.e. (m) − 1 = (m). The content of location 0002 is then checked to see if it has reached 0; when it does the program will branch to restart the monitor program. If the third loop counter is not 0 the program will jump back to the first loop again.

216 *Practical exercises*

4.8 Flow diagram

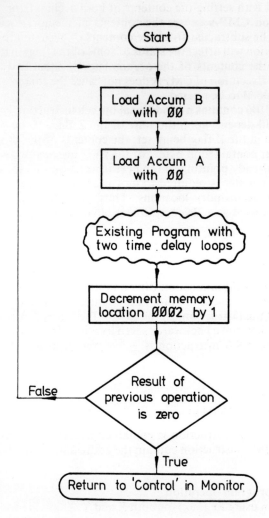

Fig. 15.7

4.9 Notes

i) When writing the program for the extra loop, look for a suitable instruction that is capable of decreasing the contents of a selected memory location. Note also whether implementing the instruction affects the condition flags (bits).

ii) The additional part of the program will start at Ø113 in place of the existing jump to monitor instruction.

iii) Before running the program, maximum loop counts will have to be put in memory locations ØØØØ, ØØØ1 and ØØØ2. Do not make the contents of ØØØ2 too large to start with. If your program has been written correctly you will be surprised at the increased time delay possible.

Exercise 5

5.1   Object
To use one of the monitor's special subroutines for outputting information to the terminal screen/printer.

5.2   Program outline
The software time loop constructed in Exercise 4 returns to control in the monitor at the end of the time delay period, and prints on the terminal a prompt. The requirement of this program is that instead of returning to control in the monitor and printing a prompt the microprocessor will print the message END. This will be achieved by using a special subroutine in the monitor that takes two hex numbers from a memory location, treats it as an 8-bit ASCII code and prints its equivalent character on the terminal printer or screen.

   The subroutine that fits this requirement of the experiment will be called 'OUT'. Refer to the documentation for individual monitors to identify a routine for this job.

5.3   Flow diagram

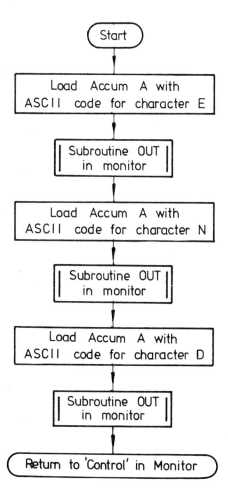

Fig. 15.8

5.4   Machine code program

Memory location	Hex code	Mnemonic	Comments
0010	45	data	ASCII code for character E.
0011	4E	data	ASCII code for character N.
0012	44	data	ASCII code for character D.
0130	8E	LDA	Load stack pointer with
0131	00 }	address	starting address of stack,
0132	FF }		i.e. 00FF.
0133	96	LDA	Load accumulator A with contents
0134	10	data	of (00)10.
0135	BD	JSR	Jump to subroutine
0136	* }	address	OUT in monitor.
0137	* }		
0138	96	LDA	Load accumulator A with the
0139	11	data	contents of (00)11.
013A	BD	JSR	Jump to subroutine
013B	* }	address	OUT.
013C	* }		
013D	96	LDA	Load accumulator A with the
013E	12	data	contents of (00)12.
013F	BD	JSR	Jump to subroutine
0140	* }	address	OUT.
0141	* }		
0142	7E	JMP	Return to control in
0143	* }	address	monitor.
0144	* }		

The following points should be noted.

1) The memory location for ASCII characters in the scratchpad RAM (0010, 0011 and 0012) and the starting point of the main program (0130) have been chosen because eventually this program will have to fit in with the addresses of the time delay program of exercise 4.

2) When using a jump to subroutine instruction, the stack pointer must be initially set to a number indicating the top address of the stack. This has been chosen as the top end of the scratchpad memory, i.e. 00FF.

5.5   Program operation
Run the program starting at 0130 and check that END is printed on the terminal.

5.6   Task 1
Write, load and then run the program employing the changes detailed below.

a)   Instead of END, the program is required to print the following:

carriage return   (CR)
line feed   (LF)
TIME UP
carriage return   (CR)
line feed   (LF)

The carriage return line feed instruction will not of course be printed on the screen but will need to be sent to the terminal.

b)   Since the number of characters to be printed is now longer, the reading of data from the character list can be improved by using indexing instead of direct addressing. A typical flow diagram is shown in Fig. 15.9.

5.7   Flow diagram

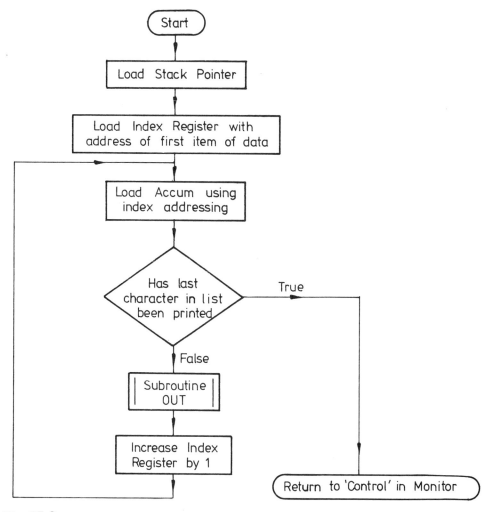

Fig. 15.9

Various methods may be used for breaking out of the program after all the required characters have been printed. One method is to place a special code at the end of the list. Each character that is loaded into the accumulator is checked and if the end of list code is found, instead of entering the subroutine OUT a jump to monitor is initiated. The special end of list code must not of course be one of the characters that is to be printed.

5.8   Task 2

Re-enter the time delay program using either two or three loops. Connect up with the TIME UP output program by placing a JMP to Ø13Ø at the end of the time delay program.

Run and check the correct operation of the complete program.

15.2   Exercises for the 8085/Z80

Exercise 1

1.1   Object

To load and run a program using immediate and direct addressing that adds two hexadecimal numbers together.

1.2   Flow diagram

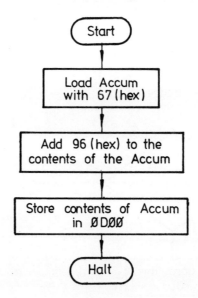

Fig. 15.10

1.3   Machine code program

Memory location	Hex code	Mnemonic	Comments
ØC7Ø	3E	MVIA	Load (immediate) accumulator
ØC71	67	data	with 67 (hex).
ØC72	C6	ADI	Add (immediate)
ØC73	96	data	96 (hex) to accumulator contents.
ØC74	32	STA	Store (direct) the contents
ØC75	ØØ	address	of accumulator in ØDØØ.
ØC76	ØD		
ØC77	76	HLT	Halt processor operation.

1.4   Loading the program

Load and check the program by using the appropriate monitor commands. Before running the program load memory location ØDØØ with ØØ (hex), so that the correct execution of the program can be checked.

1.5   Running and checking correct execution of program

Run the program using the correct monitor command procedure. Check its correct execution by examining the contents of memory location ØDØØ, i.e.

$$67 \text{ (hex) in binary form} = 01100111$$
$$96 \text{ (hex) in binary form} = 10010110$$

$$67 + 96 \text{ in binary form} = \overline{11111101}$$

$$11111101 \text{ in hexadecimal form} = \text{FD}$$

Therefore if the program has been correctly executed the contents of ØDØØ should be FD.

1.6   Task

Write and then load a machine code program for the flow diagram shown in Fig. 15.11. The starting address for the program is to be ØC7Ø. It should be noted that memory location ØCFF is to contain the hexadecimal equivalent of decimal 20.

1.7   Flow diagram

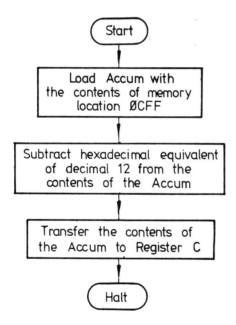

Fig. 15.11

Exercise 2

2.1   Object

To examine and run a program that adds two numbers together and uses:

i)   register addressing;
ii) register indirect addressing.

2.2   Flow diagram

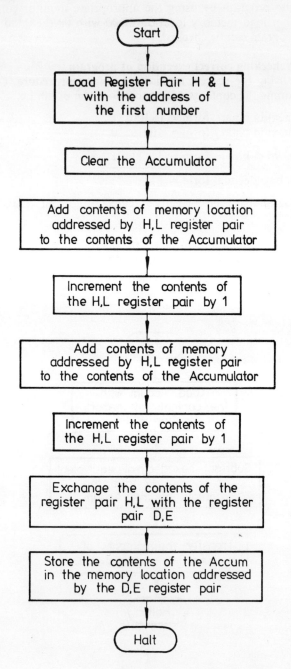

Fig. 15.12

The first number to be added is stored in ØC8Ø, the second number to be added is stored in ØC81, and the result is to be stored in ØC82.

2.3   Machine code program

Memory location	Hex code	Mnemonic	Comments
0C70	21	LXI H	Load (immediate) register
0C71	80		pair HL with 0C80.
0C72	0C	data	
0C73	AF	XRAA	Exclusively OR the accumulator with itself, i.e. clear accumulator.
0C74	86	ADD M	Add contents of memory location addressed by RP HL to accumulator.
0C75	23	INX H	Increment contents of RP HL by 1.
0C76	86	ADD M	Add contents of memory location addressed by RP HL to accumulator.
0C77	23	INX H	Increment contents of RP HL by 1.
0C78	EB	XCHG	Contents of RP HL exchanged with contents of RP DE.
0C79	12	STAX D	Store accumulator contents in memory location whose address is in RP DE.
0C7A	76	HLT	Halt processor operation.
0C80	3E	data	First number (62 decimal).
0C81	19	data	Second number (25 decimal).
0C82	00		Result (sum).

2.4   Program operation

Load, run and confirm the correct execution of the program by checking memory location 0C82. This should contain 57 (hex).

Change the data in 0C80 for numbers of your own choice and rerun the program.

2.5   Task

Write a machine code program, using register indirect addressing where appropriate, to solve the following equation:

$$Z = 2(X - Y) \quad \text{where } X > Y$$

Store X, Y and Z in 0D00, 0D01, and 0D02 respectively.

It should be noted that multiplying the binary result of $(X - Y)$ by 2 can be achieved (provided that the result is less than 128) by shifting all the bits one position to the left, and inserting a 0 in the right-hand bit position (LSB). For example:

i)   3 in binary = 00000011.
    Shifting all bits left one position and placing 0 in the least significant bit position gives:
    00000110 = 6, i.e. 3 × 2 = 6.
ii) 54 in binary = 00110110.
    Shifting left one position and inserting 0 in LSB gives:
    01101100 = 108, i.e. 54 × 2 = 108.

The instruction RLC (rotate left) in the 8085 (and Z80) causes this shift left operation to be carried out.

RLC (Rotate left)

$(An +1) \leftarrow (An); (A0) \leftarrow (A7)$
$(CY) \leftarrow (A7)$

The contents of the accumulator are rotated left one position. The low-order bit and the CY flag are both set to the value shifted out of the high-order bit position. Only the CY flag is affected.

Binary code   00000111   (opcode)

Hex code   07

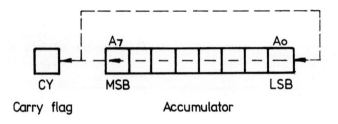

Fig. 15.13

Exercise 3

3.1 Object
To examine the operation of a program that uses conditional and unconditional jump instructions.

3.2 Program outline
The program is designed to carry out the mathematical operations of division. This consists of determining how many times one number (the divisor) can be subtracted from another number (the dividend), while still leaving a positive remainder. The program will consist of continually subtracting the divisor from the dividend until one more subtraction would leave a negative remainder. The number of times this can be carried out is the quotient; the positive number left over is the remainder.

3.3   Flow diagram

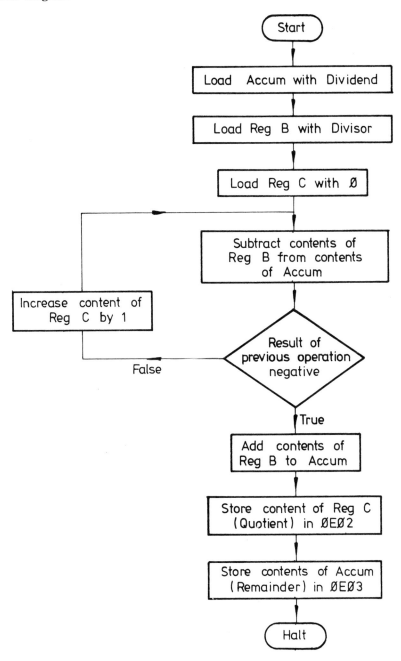

Fig. 15.14

3.4   Machine code program

Memory location	Hex code	Mnemonic	Comments
ØC7Ø	21	LXI H	Load (immediate) register pair
ØC71	ØØ ⎫		HL with ØEØØ.
ØC72	ØE ⎭ data		
ØC73	7E	MOV A, M	Load (indirect) accumulator with the contents of the memory location whose address is in RP HL, i.e. the dividend.
ØC74	23	INX H	Increment RP HL by 1.
ØC75	46	MOV B, M	Load (indirect) register B with the contents of the memory location whose address is in RP HL, i.e. the divisor.
ØC76	ØE	MVI C	Load (immediate) register C with
ØC77	ØØ	data	ØØ (hex).
ØC78	9Ø	SUB B	Subtract the contents of register B from the contents of the accumulator. Result in accumulator.
ØC79	FA	JM	Jump to ØC8Ø if contents of accumulator
ØC7A	8Ø ⎫		are negative.
ØC7B	ØC ⎭ address		
ØC7C	ØC	INR C	Increment contents of register C by 1.
ØC7D	C3	JMP	Jump unconditionally to ØC78.
ØC7E	78 ⎫		
ØC7F	ØC ⎭ address		
ØC8Ø	8Ø	ADD B	Add contents of register B to accumulator. Result in accumulator.
ØC81	23	INX H	Increment RP HL by 1.
ØC82	71	MOV M, C	Store the contents of register C in the memory location whose address is in RP HL.
ØC83	23	INX H	Increment RP HL by 1.
ØC84	77	MOV M, A	Store the contents of register A in the memory location whose address is in RP HL.
ØC86	76	HLT	Halt.

3.5   Loading the program

Load the program using the appropriate monitor commands. Place 55 hex (decimal 85) in ØEØØ, and Ø2 hex (decimal 2) in ØEØ1. Load FF into the quotient and remainder locations so that the correct operation of the program can be checked.

Memory location	Hex code	Mnemonic	Comments
ØE00	55		Dividend
ØE01	02		Divisor
ØE02	FF		Quotient
ØE03	FF		Remainder

3.6   Running and checking execution of program
Execute the program starting at ØC70. Check the contents of ØE02, which should be 42
(85 ÷ 2 = 42), and ØE03, which should be Ø1 (remainder 1).
    Now choose your own values for dividend and divisor and rerun the program. Do not
choose a value or the dividend greater than decimal 127.

3.7   Task
Write a program to multiply two numbers n and m together by the process of adding 'm
lots of n'.
    The two numbers n and m are to be held in store locations ØD00 and ØD01 respectively,
with the result in ØD02. Program execution should start at ØC72.
    The program must check to see whether the result is larger than 255 (maximum
number possible with 8 bits) and if so give an indication to this effect. One simple method
of achieving this objective is to load memory location ØD02 with ØØ hex if the result is
larger than 255. Provided that m or n is never 0 this will provide a simple means of
indicating if an overflow has occurred.
    Test the program for data that will produce normal execution and an overflow
condition.

3.8   Flow diagram

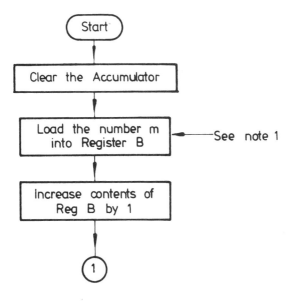

Fig. 15.15   (continued overleaf)

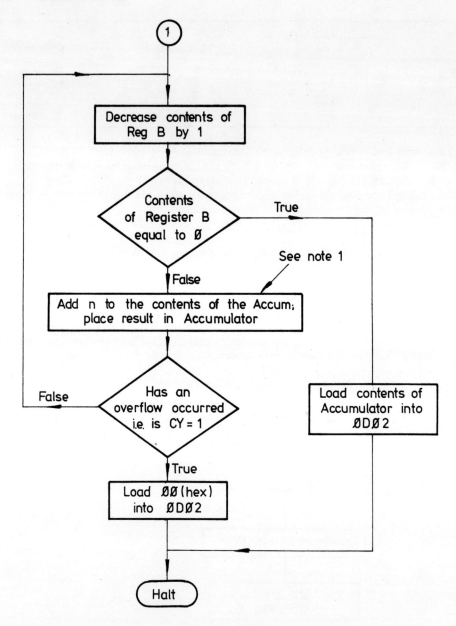

Note 1 – Use H & L register for this operation

Fig. 15.15   (continued from p. 227)

15.3   Exercises for the 6502

Exercise 1

1.1   Object
To add two hex numbers by using immediate and direct addressing modes.

1.2   Flow diagram

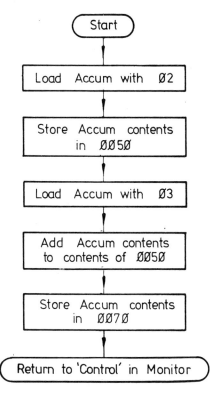

Fig. 15.16

1.3   Machine code program

Memory location	Hex code	Mnemonic	Comments
01FF	18	CLC	Clear carry bit.
0200	A9	LDA	Load accumulator (immediate)
0201	02	data	with 02.
0202	85	STA Z	Store accumulator (direct)
0203	50	address	in location 0050.
0204	A9	LDA	Load accumulator (immediate)
0205	03	data	with 03.
0206	65	ADC Z	Add with carry (direct) accumulator
0207	50	address	with contents of location 0050.
0208	85	STA Z	Store accumulator (direct)
0209	70	address	in location 0070.
020A	4C	JMP	
020B	*	address	Return to control
020C	*		in monitor.

After execution location 0070 should contain 05. If it does not, but instead holds 06, ensure that the carry bit of the accumulator is cleared by using the opcode 18 as the first in the program. Before running the program it is a good idea to zeroise location 0070.

1.4   Task
In what form of arithmetic was the answer presented? Two are possible — decimal or hexadecimal. Investigate, preceding the above program with the 'set decimal mode' flag instruction, F8, or the 'clear decimal mode' flag instruction, D8. The instruction F8 causes the result of a binary arithmetic sum to be converted to binary coded decimal (BCD).

Exercise 2

2.1   Object
1)   To add two numbers in locations 0270 and 0271, leaving the result in 0300, and using the direct extended mode throughout.
2)   To add two numbers in locations 0070 and 0071, leaving the results in 0072, using pre- and post-indexed indirect addressing.

2.2   Flow diagram (1)

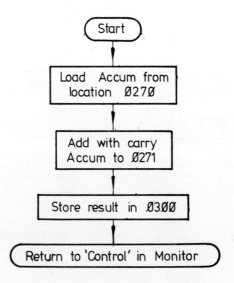

Fig. 15.17

Check that your program first clears the carry bit, and set the decimal mode flag.

2.3 Machine code program using extended direct mode

Memory location	Hex code	Mnemonic	Comments
0200	18	CLC	Clear the carry flag.
0201	F8	SED	Set decimal mode.
0202	AD	LDA	Load the accumulator
0203	70	address	from location 0270.
0204	02		
0205	6D	ADC	Add with carry the contents
0206			of the accumulator to the contents
	71	address	of location 0271 leaving the result
0207	02		in the accumulator.
0208	8D	STA	Store the contents of the accumulator
0209	00	address	in location 0300.
020A	03		
020B	4C	JMP	
020C	*	address	Return to control in monitor.
020D	*		

2.4 Flow diagram (2)

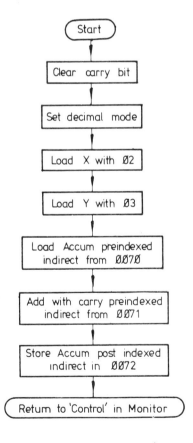

Fig. 15.18

2.5   Machine code program using pre- and post-indexing

Memory location	Hex code	Mnemonic	Comments
0200	18	CLC	Clear the carry flag.
0201	F8	SED	Set decimal mode.
0202	A2	LDX	Load the X register immediate
0203	02	data	with 02.
0204	A0	LDY	Load the Y register immediate
0205	03	data	with 03.
0206	A1	LDAI, X	Load accumulator pre-indexed
0207	4E	address	indirect from location 0070.
0208	61	ADCI, X	Add the accumulator pre-indexed
0209	50	address	indirect to the contents of location 0071.
020A	91	STAI, Y	Store the contents of the accumulator
020B	54	address	post-indexed indirect in location 0072.
020C	4C	NOP	
020D	*	address	Return to control in monitor.
020E	*		
020F			

In order for this program to work it is necessary to:

> load location 0050 with 70
> load location 0051 with 00
> load location 0052 with 71
> load location 0053 with 00
> load location 0054 with 6F
> load location 0055 with 00
> load location 0070 with first number
> load location 0071 with second number

After program execution, check the contents of 0072 for the correct answer.

2.6   Task
Write a program to load the accumulator post-indexed indirect from location 0072 and add this number to the contents of location 0071 post-indexed indirect, storing the result in location 0073 pre-indexed indirect.

Exercise 3

3.1   Object
To write a program that uses relative branch and conditional test instructions.

3.2   Program outline
A time delay loop will be the means of illustrating relative branching techniques. When the program is run, the processor will execute a loop of instructions a specified number of times. Since each operation takes time (a number of machine cycles), timing functions

can be achieved. When the processor finally breaks out of the loop it will be forced to return control to the monitor program.

Use will be made of a memory location and the Y register in addition to the accumulator.

3.3   Flow diagram

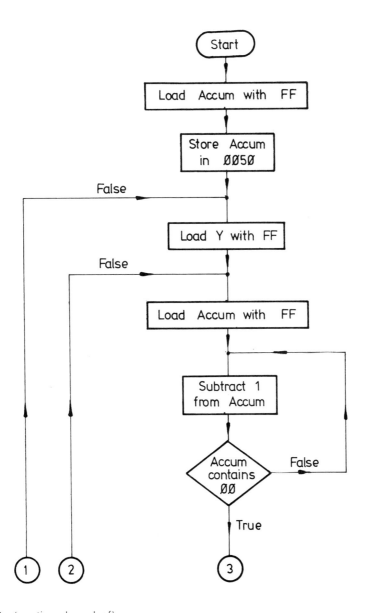

Fig. 15.19   (continued overleaf)

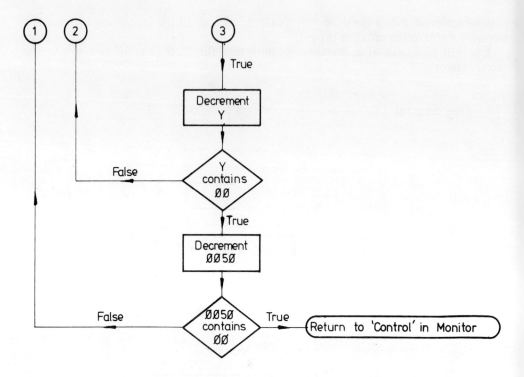

Fig. 15.19   (continued from p. 233)

3.4 Machine code program

Memory location	Hex code	Mnemonic	Comments
0200	A9	LDA, I	Load the accumulator
0201	FF	data	immediate with FF.
0202	85	STA, Z	Store the accumulator
0203	50	address	contents in (00)50.
0204	A0	LDY, I	Load the Y register
0205	FF	data	immediate with FF.
0206	A9	LDA, I	Load the accumulator
0207	FF	data	immediate with FF.
0208	E9	SBC	Subtract 1 from the
0209	01	data	accumulator.
020A	D0	BNE	Branch back to 0208
020B	FC	data	if accumulator contents are not 00.
020C	88	DEY	Decrement Y.
020D	D0	BNE	Branch back to 0206 if
020E	F7	data	Y does not contain 00.
020F	C6	DEC	Decrement location (00)50.
0210	50	address	
0211	D0	BNE	Branch back to 0204
0212	F1	data	if (00)50 does not contain 00.
0213	4C	JMP	Jump to
0214	*	address	control in monitor.
0215	*		

3.5   Relative and arithmetic instructions used

SBC   Subtracts the data (byte 2) from the contents of the accumulator, with carry.

BNE   Branches if the zero flag in the status register indicates that an operation on a register leaves other than zero in that register. Byte 2 indicates a forward or backward jump relative to the present program counter contents expressed in 2's complement hexadecimal form.

DEY   Decrements the contents of the Y register.

DEC   Decrements the contents of a memory location in base page zero specified by byte 2.

3.6   Task

The program given will produce a time delay of about 1 minute. By changing the values loaded into location 0050, the Y register, and the accumulator, check the relative effect of each on the delay period.

Index

Index